A QUANTUM BOOK

This book is produced by
Quantum Publishing Ltd.
6 Blundell Street
London N7 9BH

This edition printed 2003

ISBN 1-86160-677-X

QUMSBE

Printed in China by
Leefung-Asco Printers Limited

Special thanks to Bush Boake Allen Ltd,Essex
for supplying the cosmetic containers shown
throughout this book

BE BEAUTIFUL

Linda Sonntag

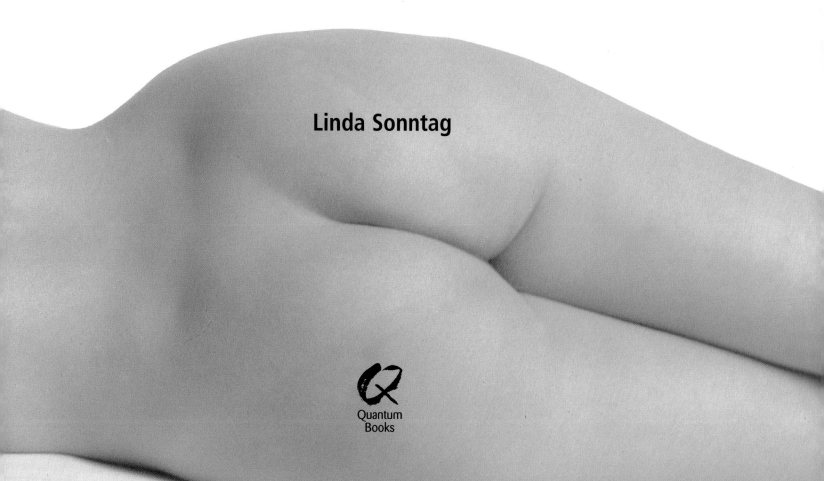

Q

Quantum
Books

CONTENTS

Introduction

Today beauty is more than skin deep — it's feeling good as well as looking good. A healthy diet, with plenty of fresh fruit and vegetables and lots of mineral water to drink, regular exercise, fresh air and sleep will give you a sound foundation for your beauty routines.

Making the most of your looks need not cost you a fortune or be endlessly time-consuming. Once you have discovered the individual requirements of your own hair and skin type and acquired the simple skill of applying just the right amount of make-up, caring for your looks will become second nature. But there's always room to experiment with new ideas.

This book aims to help you get the best from your natural resources and show you how skin care, hair care and body care can achieve stunning results and keep you looking — and feeling — younger, longer.

SKIN

Skin

Skin is a living organ that covers the whole body. It is the body's largest organ, measuring about 1.5m² (1.5yd²). Its thickness varies from .05mm ($\frac{1}{500}$in) on the eyelids, where it is at its most delicate and translucent, to .65mm ($\frac{1}{40}$in) on the soles of the feet, where it is at its toughest. With the exception of the palms of the hands and the soles of the feet, the skin is covered with hair follicles.

The skin's function is to protect the body, to help regulate body temperature by perspiring, and to excrete waste products such as water and salt.

Skin consists of three layers: the outer layer, called the epidermis; the dermis, which is full of glands and blood vessels; and the hypoderm, a fatty tissue that acts mainly as a cushion between the dermis and the muscles beneath. The epidermis has no blood vessels, and this means that it can heal without a

Skin

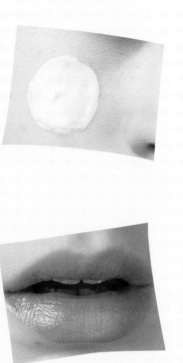

trace. Its surface cells are flat and horny; they are, in fact, dead, and are constantly being shed. They flake off with friction from clothes or bed sheets, or get washed away in the bath. Other cells from beneath replace them. If the skin is exposed without a protective cream to harsh conditions, such as blistering sun, biting wind or stinging cold, cells will be shed at a faster rate and the skin will become red and raw.

The dermis, being full of blood vessels, scars when it is damaged. It is responsible for the changes of colour that signal our moods. Emotions trigger off a set of physical and chemical reactions in the body. The blood vessels in the dermis dilate and we flush with anger, embarrassment or pleasure; they shrink and we blanch with fear or nausea. The sebaceous glands in the dermis secrete sebum, one of the skin's natural moisturisers. A balanced skin occurs when sebum is secreted in exactly the right proportion. The skin will then be soft, supple and fine-textured. It will be smooth and blemish-free, rose-tinted and translucent. A perfect complexion is a rare phenomenon, but fortunately a lot can be done to improve an imperfect one. Underactive sebaceous glands cause dry skin, and overactive ones, oily skin.

Hormones circulating in the bloodstream stimulate the pigment cells to produce colour. They also control the production of sweat and sebum. This explains the changes in the skin's appearance at different times in the menstrual cycle and during and after pregnancy. Hormonal imbalance, which is inevitable at the onset of puberty, can cause enlarged pores — a condition that often produces blackheads and acne.

The dermis also contains the nerves, which are dense in some areas of the body and sparse in others. The concentration of nerves can also vary from person to person, making some people more sensitive to tickling in, say, the ribs, and others to tickling in the neck or the soles of the feet.

Skin, our contact with the elements, is bound to show the effects of use and abuse, and to reflect the process of ageing. Skin can age prematurely because of illness, an unhealthy diet, heavy smoking or drinking, or over-exposure to heat, cold or a humid climate. But if you are to keep a clear, smooth and young skin, you should start caring for it properly — with a twice-daily cleansing routine — as early as possible.

There is no doubt that skin is at its best while young and fresh. A healthy child enjoys a complexion of peachy softness and creamy texture. But youth is not always a guarantee of problem-free skin. Even babies can suffer from rashes and allergies. Puberty is often a bad time for skin. The hormonal upheaval in the body is conducive to acne and also stimulates the follicles into producing unwanted facial hair. This will usually fall out as the body settles down, and it can be disguised by bleaching.

Skin

During the early 20s your skin should look at its best. This is the time to watch out for allergies, that could continue into maturity, to different brands of make-up and to drugs (such as 'the Pill'), detergents, chemicals and insecticides. In the late 20s and early 30s the skin will begin to lose the bloom of youth. You should watch out for a tendency to dryness and change to a richer moisturizer. Anyone who has always had a dry skin will notice fine lines appearing as the 30s advance — dry skins tend to age more quickly than oily ones. Tiny, broken blood vessels may appear around the nose or on the cheeks. These can be disguised by skilful make-up.

As hormone-production slows down in the 40s, the skin begins to lose its tone, strength and elasticity. The protein fibres in the dermis sag, leaving the epidermis undernourished. Wrinkles and bags form, and the skin dries, becoming loose and flabby. In the late 50s the skin often develops brown spots as the colour agent, or pigment forms deposits. Now is the time to watch out for skin cancer. There are four basic types of this disease, which is often caused by over-exposure to the sun. It manifests itself as brown or red blotches on the face and is usually responsive to treatment, although some scarring may remain. The most serious kind is malignant melanoma. A brown, black or blue blotch appears on the skin and indicates the presence of a growth. This must be removed to prevent spreading.

Many women, during and after the menopause, experiment with hormone creams for wrinkles around the eyes and throat. These are said to plump out the flesh beneath the wrinkles and indeed they do seem to work, though the effects may last only a couple of hours. Hormone creams are very expensive, and if you do decide to try them, you may find it worth while to alternate daily between the hormone cream and your usual moisturizer to spread the cost. Or you can use the hormone cream for three-month periods in order to become more aware of its benefits.

Whatever your age, the vital daily routine for every face is the same. You will need a cleanser, a toner and a moisturizer. You will also need an eye make-up remover. From time to time you can refresh you skin with different masks, and as you get into your 30s you'd be well advised to invest in eye and throat creams as well as a nourishing night cream.

Before you stock your dressing table with these essential products, you will need to discover your skin type. The perfect complexion is supple and translucent, moist without being oily. Most people have skins that are dry, oily, or a combination of both. An oily skin will leave a transparent mark on a piece of tissue paper pressed against it; a dry skin will tend to flake. Many women have an oily forehead, nose and chin, and dry skin on their cheeks. Choose the products that are suited to your skin type.

Skin

The way in which you apply your cleanser, toner and moisturizer is important. Facial skin, especially around the eyes and on the neck, is very delicate, and must be treated with care. The muscles beneath, too, should be encouraged to stay elastic and mobile, as sagging causes wrinkles. Don't scrub at your face — broken veins as well as wrinkles will be the result.

If you prefer soap and water to a cleanser, choose a mild, unperfumed soap and keep it away from your eyes. Use lukewarm water, rinse thoroughly and finish with a splash of cold water to close the pores.

For an oily skin, choose a milk or lotion. A cream cleanser is best suited to a dry or combination skin. Remove all traces of soap or cleanser after use.

The next step is toning. A toner will remove all traces of grease from the skin, refresh it and close the pores. Make sure you choose an alcohol-free toner if you have a sensitive skin.

Follow with your moisturizer to nourish and protect your skin. A heavier night cream should be used before you go to bed, especially on drier skins.

A face mask is a good tonic for a tired skin. It will remove dirt and flakes of dead surface skin and leave your face feeling vibrant and fresh. Never put a mask near your eyes where your skin is at its most delicate. There are many types of mask available over the counter, so make sure that you choose one that's right for your skin type.

If you want to make a mask at home, avocado mashed with a little olive oil provides ideal nourishment for a dry skin, while slivers of cucumber pressed lightly onto your face and over your eyelids are a good refresher. Ground oatmeal mixed to a paste with water will make a gentle 'scrub' to get rid of dead skin.

Note; when using propreitary facial scrubs follow the pack instructions and take care not to scrub too hard, or to use too often, as excessive use may damage the skin.

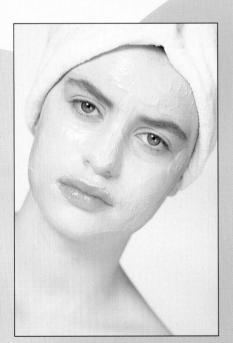

Top: a light home-made mask of avocado pulp, thinned with olive oil will nourish a dry skin. Bottom: a proprietary clay mask. Applied evenly avoiding the eye area it will lift off surface skin debris and tone the skin.

Skin Problems

Adolescence often causes problems for the complexion. Spots, blackheads and acne all beset a person whose hormonal balance is changing, causing the glands to produce too much sebum. These conditions do not mean that you have a dirty skin, but they can be minimized by careful and frequent washing with a mild soap to stop bacteria from spreading. A facial scrub will often remove blackheads, especially if you have opened the pores by steaming your face over a bowl of water first. You can help a spot to dry out more quickly by dabbing at it continually with antiseptic. This is a much better way of dealing with it than squeezing, which can result in bruising (an ugly red patch is hardly an improvement on a spot), bleeding and broken veins. If you have acne, you should see your doctor. Antibiotic treatment can often be prescribed, but, sadly, sometimes the only answer is, 'You'll grow out of it'. Check your diet and cut out sweet and greasy foods. Eat more fresh fruit and raw vegetables and drink plenty

After cleansing the face, position your face in the steam from a bowl of just-boiled water. This will warm the surface of the skin and help the removal of blackheads. Avoid doing this for any length of time if you have broken veins — alternatively protect the cheeks with pads of cotton wool stuck on with face cream.

Skin Problems

of mineral water. Keep your face scrupulously clean.

Unwanted hair can be dealt with in several ways: bleaching, shaving, waxing, depilation and electrolysis.

● Bleaching is very effective if you want to conceal a fine down of hair on face or arms. Warning; only use a bleach cream product specifically formulated for use on the face. Household bleach is not suitable. Do a patch test on the inside of your lower arm and leave it for an hour to make sure that there's no irritation before you apply the bleach to your face. Follow manufacturer's instructions carefully.

● Shaving removes hair quite satisfactorily from underarms and legs. You will need to shave regularly, with a shaving cream to avoid soreness. Don't apply antiperspirant to a shaved armpit straight away — it may sting.

● Waxing can be done at home, but it's best to learn how by having treatment done professionally first, as it's easy to burn yourself with the hot wax. Stripping off the wax is quite painful, but regrowth will not appear for about three weeks. Wax treatment is suitable for legs and bikini line.

● Depilation is useful for underarm and leg hair removal. A patch test (as with bleach products) with the depilatory cream is advisable to avoid soreness. These creams break off the hair shaft just below the skin. Wash thoroughly after use and apply moisturiser.

● Electrolysis is the only way to remove unwanted hair permanently, and this must be done by an expert. Each hair is treated individually with a fine needle that has an electric current running through it. It's a lengthy and costly business, but often worth it if you have, say, a heavy growth of coarse, dark hair on your upper lip.

There are many ways of disguising body hair using products such as bleach to disguise growth on face or arms. When using hot wax or depilatory creams the hair is removed and regrowth occurs more slowly than shaving which needs to be done more regularly.

HAIR

Hair

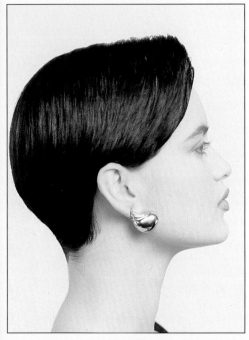

A well-kept cap of hair like the one above depends on regular, expert cutting and conditioning to maintain the shine.

Your hair is a valuable natural fibre and to get it looking at its best you should treat it with as much care as you would silk or wool. Fortunately, hair is very resilient. An average single hair can be stretched by 20 to 30 per cent its normal length, a force that would snap most textile fabrics. Wet hair needs less force to stretch it and is more vulnerable to damage. If your hair is in poor condition because of neglect, or if it has been subjected to harsh treatment, all is not lost. With care and attention you should be able to restore its bounce and glossy sheen.

Hair grows all over the body except on the palms of the hands and the soles of the feet. The average adult scalp sprouts about 100,000 hairs, quantity varying with the number of strands. Blondes who have the largest number of strands — up to 150,000 — tend to have hair that looks finer than brunettes or redheads. Texture and curliness of the hair is due mainly to different types of keratin in hair and heredity.

A single hair lives and grows for between two and six years — in some cases for 20 years — though, technically speaking, the hair shaft is dead matter and only the root is alive. The shaft emerges from the papilla, a nodule at the base of the hair follicle below the surface of the skin. Hair-growth cannot be stopped by pulling a hair out by the root, because the papilla will eventually produce a new hair.

Hair is approximately 97 per cent protein and 3 per cent moisture. So the importance of protein in the diet for healthy hair is obvious. Each hair is made up of three layers. The inner core, or medulla, is the 'marrow' of the hair and is soft and spongy. It can deteriorate in old age and be damaged by drugs and chemicals. In some cases it is missing altogether and the hair becomes thin and brittle.

The medulla is surrounded by the cortex, which is composed of long, thin, fibrous cells that give the hair its elasticity. The cortex also contains the pigment that gives the hair its natural colour. Pigments are red, yellow and black, and a mixture of these over the entire head gives the hair its individual shade. If no pigment is present, the hair is white. There is no such thing as grey hair — this is an illusion caused by white hairs appearing amongst hairs of the original colour. The cortex is the part of the hair that responds to chemicals intended to curl, straighten or colour it.

The outer layer, the cuticle, is formed of hard scales of keratin that overlap like tiles on a roof. The cuticle protects the hair shaft. When the scales are lying smoothly, they reflect the light and give the hair its shine; they also trap the oil that gives the hair its lustre. This oil, or sebum, the hair's natural conditioner, is produced by the sebaceous gland attached to the hair follicle. The hair is lubricated by

You can maintain a sleek and elegant look if the hair is cut regularly, like this neat bob which shows off the perfect condition of the hair.

the sebum, but the ends of longer hair will never be reached; you will need to use a conditioner and trim off split ends. Lubrication is also stimulated by the tiny muscles around the follicle. It is these muscles that are responsible for the hair 'standing on end' through cold or fear.

Hair begins to grow before birth, but it is a myth that it continues to grow after death. It is simply the last part of the body to decay. Everyone loses, on average, 100 hairs a day, these are replaced, except in the case of thinning hair, by new growth. Hairs grow at the rate of about 1cm per month. Strangely, it grows faster in summer than in winter, and faster during the day than the night. Women's hair grows faster than men's. Cutting hair does not accelerate growth, though shaving hair under the arms and on the legs may make it appear coarser because it then grows with a blunted end.

A baby may be born with very little hair or with a lot. Its hair may fall out in the first weeks of life and then begin to grow again, and its hair type and colour may change. But by the time the child is about three, it will have settled down with the hair type it will have for life.

Hormonal changes in the body and an active life are often the cause of lank and greasy hair in teenagers. A diet that is low in fats, sugar and carbohydrates should be encouraged. Adolescents should also be encouraged to wash their hair as often as they want — even twice a day won't harm the hair, so long as a gentle shampoo is used and the hair is allowed to dry naturally. Conditioner need be applied only at the ends of long hair.

Dandruff is another condition that can arise during the teens. If frequent and thorough shampooing with a mild shampoo does not help, try a medicated brand. Dandruff in the teens is sometimes caused by dirt, grease and shampoo being left behind on the scalp.

Split ends should be trimmed off. These can be exacerbated by the excessive use of hairdryers and heated styling equipment.

During the 20s, when life gets into full swing, it may be tempting to take advantage of the fact that your hair is enjoying maximum health and expect it to bounce back of its own accord every time you perm or colour it, or every time you expose it to holiday sun or the chlorine of a swimming pool. Use a nourishing conditioner on damaged hair or rub in warm olive oil or a wax cream; then wrap

Hair

your head in plastic film, tie it in a scarf and leave it for as long as you can — overnight if possible. Protect your hair from the sun under a hat or scarf. If you go swimming, always rinse salt water or chlorine out of your hair straight away, then shampoo and condition. A conditioning gel is an excellent idea for keen swimmers and sunbathers. Apply it generously to your hair before you go to the beach to achieve a wet look that will be quite in place and will protect your hair all day.

Pregnancy affects the hair in different ways. Some women find that it makes it more lustrous, while other, less fortunate, women lose quantities of hair. Some pregnant women find that their perm loses its bounce. Nothing can be done about this, but a healthy diet will ensure that the hair regains its former condition as soon as possible after the birth.

A tendency to dry and brittle hair is common in the 30s, mainly due to the normal ageing process. It is sometimes the result of perming and colouring, but can be due to stress. This is the time when the body's functions begin

A long cut like this one can be given lift and swept dramatically into shape with gel. The hair stays in perfect condition when it is trimmed regularly to remove split ends.

A long style has been tamed with a soft perm. The hair is kept in perfect shape and condition by allowing it to dry naturally and by running the fingers through it as it dries for this soft, bouncy look.

to slow down and the production of sebum is reduced. This is the time, too, when most people discover their first grey hairs. These are actually white hairs, which look grey when mingled in with hairs of your natural colour. Many women in their 40s decide to disguise their grey hairs with a specially formulated rinse. At this age you should use a rich shampoo and pay special attention to conditioning. A wax or oil treatment once a week will bring life back to your hair. Henna treatments restore the shine to dull hair; but use one without a colourant on grey or white hair, or you may be dazzled by the result.

During the menopause, hormonal imbalance and the emotional stress that often goes along with it can cause significant hair-loss, while facial hair may coarsen or grow darker. Many women find that hormone replacement therapy (HRT) keeps their hair in good condition and stops it from falling out. At the same time it benefits the skin, slowing down the deepening of wrinkles. It has other advantages, too. It helps the flesh to stay firmer longer and the spine to stay erect.

Whether to opt for HRT is a decision for each women to make in consultation with her doctor. If you decide against it, you should be able to avoid the distress of hair-loss by keeping to a healthy diet, taking frequent exercise to stimulate the blood circulation, keeping the scalp scrupulously clean and using nourishing conditioners.

Shampooing

However beautiful your hair is naturally, you need to treat it well. The first essential is regular shampooing. How often you wash your hair depends entirely on you. Wash it as often as you need to keep the scalp scrupulously clean. A mild pH-balanced shampoo, correctly formulated for your hair type, is best: it will neither irritate the scalp nor disturb the acid/alkaline balance of the hair. Don't be tempted to use detergents, such as washing-up liquid, as these will strip the hair of its natural oils. One shampooing will normally suffice. Use warm water from a spray to wet your hair thoroughly. Then pour a little shampoo into your cupped hand and massage it firmly, but gently, all over your scalp and through your hair. Rinse very thoroughly again from the spray, until the water runs from your hair perfectly free of soap.

In an emergency, you can use a dry shampoo. Rub it into the hair and scalp and leave if for a minute or two then brush it out. Alternatively dab your scalp and hair with cotton wool soaked in eau-de-cologne. Both methods get rid of grease, but, of course, neither is as satisfactory as a good wash. If you have run out of shampoo, try using the yolks of three eggs, beaten, instead.

Conditioning

There are three basic types of conditioner. Creams and rinses moisturise and add gloss as well as getting rid of static to make hair more manageable. A deep-treatment conditioner will also nourish and bring back life to dull or damaged hair. Deep wax or oil treatments should be left on the hair, under plastic film and a towel, for as long as possible (overnight is ideal). They should be used once a week, or once a month, as necessary.

Ordinary conditioners, the creams and rinses, are applied in the same way as shampoo. Massage gently into the scalp and run your fingers through your hair so that it gets to the ends as well as the roots. Leave the conditioner on for a minute or two — perhaps while you soak in the bath or shower — then rinse thoroughly with warm water. A final cool-water rinse flattens the keratin scales on the hair shaft and makes the hair shinier.

Shampoos and conditioners come in many scents and colours. Shampoos are basically mild detergents with thickeners, colour and perfume added. Cream conditioners, conditioning rinses and wax treatment creams condition the hair and neutralise any charge so that they make the hair more manageable.

Hair Care at Home

Drying

Whatever method you choose for drying your hair, you should first comb it through. Start at the tip, easing the tangles gently out, and work back along the hairshaft. If you start at the scalp, you'll only create fiercer tangles lower down. Take your time and don't tug. Carelessness will damage your hair. Use a wide-toothed comb on wet hair — it will free the tangles more easily than a fine toothed one. Leave your brush, if you use one at all (they often cause static), until your hair is dry. A brush will snarl wet hair and stretch it to breaking point.

The best way to dry your hair is to leave it and let it dry naturally. To add body and increase the manageability of fine hair, use a mousse or gel. Squirt the mousse or squeeze the gel into a cupped hand. Rub your palms together, then spread the mousse or gel over the hair. Comb through into the style you want, or comb back from your face to give extra lift. Another way of giving your hair lift is to scrunch it up with your fingers as it dries. If you haven't time to let your hair dry naturally, blot and squeeze dry with a towel before combing out. You can then set or blow dry.

To set, first apply the setting lotion of your choice, then divide your hair with a tail comb into even sections. Don't put too much hair on any one roller. Curly hair will get even curlier on small rollers; so use larger ones for a healthy bounce. Thin hair needs to be rolled into a tighter curl on smaller rollers. Hold the hair away from the head at an angle of 90 degrees and wind it firmly, but

All hair types should be dried with care — hair stretches when wet and can be easily damaged. Start by blotting the hair well using a soft, dry towel — this will absorb most of the moisture. Then preferably leave the hair to dry naturally or blow dry with care.

21

Hair Care at Home

Shapers are brightly coloured bendy rods of lightweight foam and avoid the damage sometimes inflicted by rollers. Wrap hair round the shapers while still slightly damp, bend over the end of the rods to secure then allow hair to dry naturally. They are heat resistant so you can use a hairdryer if you wish.

without stretching, onto the roller. Secure it with a pin. Use Sellotape or clips for curls around the face. If you don't like the idea of rollers and pins, try the new 'shapers'. They are bendy sticks round which you wind your hair. You then twist the shaper round on itself to hold the hair in place. Shapers act on the same principle as the rags that were used to curl Goldilocks-type hair. They are colourful and look pretty, which is more than can be said for rollers; so you won't feel embarrassed if you're caught wearing them.

If you set your hair, you should wait until it is completely dry before taking out the rollers. If you are sitting under a drier, turn it off before your hair is quite dry and let the drying process finish naturally. Excessive heat is always damaging to the hair.

Comb each lock of hair through as you remove the rollers, starting at the nape of the neck and working up to the forehead. If the result is too hard, and you can see the partings left by the rollers, you may need a gentle back-brushing to disguise your handiwork, but be careful not to comb or brush too vigorously, as this will break the hairshafts. A light hairspray, applied directly from the aerosol or sprayed onto a brush and run through the hair if your style is smooth and sleek, will help the hair to hold its shape longer.

Most modern styles rely, not on a set, but on a superb cut and clever blow-drying. When a hairdresser blow-dries your hair it takes next to no time and looks very simple indeed; but as you will find when you start to do it yourself, it needs a little practice. Choose a plastic wand brush with widely spaced, springy bristles and hold it in your right hand if you are right-handed. Work from the nape, pinning the damp hair on top of your head out of the way. Divide the hair into sections and wind it over the brush. Blow with the hairdryer from the root to the end of the strands. Don't hold it too close to the hair and keep it moving all the time, always in the direction of the hair growth. Work your way round the sides of your head and finish off with the crown.

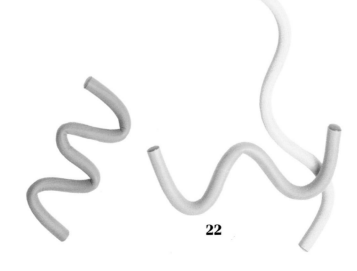

Oily hair

Over-active sebaceous glands produce oily hair and skin. Oily hair is most often fine hair, and the fineness aggravates the problem of lank and lifeless locks. You should watch your diet and cut out greasy foods. Plenty of fresh fruit and salads with lots of mineral water to drink will help. It will come as a great relief to you to know that it is a fallacy that frequent shampooing makes the hair even more greasy. If you spent your adolescent years in misery because you were told you should only wash your hair every three days, even though it was dreadfully greasy for two of them, forget it. Your hair looks good only when it is clean. So wash it as often as you like, even twice a day if the weather is hot and sticky or very windy.

Use a mild shampoo and apply a cream conditioner only to the ends of long hair. The best after-shampoo rinse for an oily head is an astringent one. Try a homemade herbal rinse or simply dilute some cider vinegar (stronger vinegars will leave you smelling like a fish-and-chip shop) in lukewarm water and sluice it over your head after washing your hair. The acid in it will counteract the grease and will also flatten the keratin scales on the hairshafts and give extra shine.

Another very useful preparation for oily hair, especially when it is fine and flyaway, is a hair gel or mousse. Even if you let your hair dry naturally after applying it, you will find that it gives extra bounce and texture.

Dry hair

Dry hair is caused by under-active sebaceous glands or by over-exposure to wind, salt or chlorinated water, or heat. Heat is the most common source of damage to the hair, whether from the sun, from hairdryers or heated styling appliances, or from central heating. Frequent perming and bleaching may also make the hair brittle and unmanageable. If your hair has a constant tendency to break, apparently for none of these reasons, check with your doctor; the cause may be drugs that you are being prescribed.

Washing dry hair will not strip it of its natural oils. Whatever your hair type, your prime objective must be to keep the hair clean; and if you use the correct products, gently massaged into the scalp, you will be able to restore shine to even the driest hair. Use a rich shampoo, rinse clean with lukewarm water and follow with a cream conditioner, combing it through to the ends of the hair. Once a week give yourself a warm olive oil or wax cream treatment. Massage the oil or cream well into the scalp, comb the hair through and cover in cling film since this will hold in heat which helps the treatment to penetrate the hair shaft, then wrap in a towel or scarf. Leave it on for at least an hour, or overnight if you can. Wash out the oil with two latherings of shampoo and condition as normal. This treatment is especially good for bleached or heat-damaged hair.

Hair Care at Home

Dandruff

The best treatment for dandruff is to use an anti-dandruff shampoo as directed. Use of a mild or medicated shampoo may also help. The most important thing is to keep the scalp scrupulously clean. Make sure that your diet is a healthy one and includes white meat or fish, eggs, cheese, fresh fruit and raw vegetables. Drink plenty of mineral water. Take exercise to help overcome tension. If dandruff persists, visit your doctor.

Excessive hair-loss

Normally about 100 hairs will be lost from the head each day. If your hair-loss is more severe, the first thing to do is check your diet. Your hair will never be luxuriant if your diet is poor. Try to get plenty of fresh air and exercise, as well as lots of sleep. Use a comb, not a brush. Slightly more hair-loss in spring and autumn is quite natural. Keep your hair short — it will look fuller and will prevent the weight of long hair from causing more of it to fall out. See your doctor or a trichologist if you are upset by this problem.

Split and broken hair

If your hair is in very bad condition, and given to splitting and breaking, the cause may be excessive perming or bleaching. Or it may be careless use of heated styling appliances or severe exposure to a merciless sun. Breaks and splits can never be mended; your hair will need a good professional cut and regular trimming until new growth has replaced the damaged hair. In the meantime, treat your hair gently and give it a weekly deep-conditioning treatment to restore its shine and disguise the worst of the damage. If you wish to perm or colour your hair yourself at this stage, take care to follow the manufacturer's instructions. If, when your hair is in better condition, you decide to perm or colour it professionally, always get your hairdresser to do a strand test first.

Long hair is a valuable asset and needs to be treated very gently. If you are contemplating a change of colour, or a perm, always take your hairdresser's advice and don't attempt anything drastic at home.

To keep long hair in top condition and avoid broken and split ends, you will need to be aware that your number one enemy is heat. The tips of your hair are probably about four years old, and four years of regular treatment with hairdryers and various electrical styling appliances may result in some damage. The ends of long hair should be trimmed regularly to remove split ends, and your hair should be allowed to dry naturally if possible. If you want to add bounce or curl without endangering your hair by the constant use of heated rollers, try using bending shapers, or, if you can't find these in the shops, the old-fashioned rag technique. Both work on the same principle; used on slightly damp hair they will give movement, while on dry hair they will give bounce. They are particularly effective when used in conjunction with a styling mousse. To dress out the hair, finger the curls apart, starting from the nape and sides of the head and finishing with the crown. Brush through for a fluffier style. More time-consuming, but very spectacular, is the pre-Raphaelite look. This is achieved by making tiny plaits — as many as you can manage — all over the head. It is best done on damp hair and left overnight. In the morning, undo the plaits and carefully finger through.

Long hair that is kept in good condition is extremely versatile to style: here long hair has been dressed into (from top to bottom, then right), a softly waved bob, a sophisticated swept back style, an upswept yet fun look and an elegant chignon.

Black Afro Hair

The range of beauty products for black hair and the number of hairdressers who specialize in Afro styling has increased dramatically over the past ten years. As with any other hair type, a balanced diet is needed for healthy hair, but black hair has extra requirements, because it is coarse, fragile, dry and highly susceptible to atmospheric conditions.

Not so long ago, the answer to brittle, dull and unmanageable black hair used to be a thick coating of oil applied after infrequent washing. It was supposed to act as a straightener and a gloss. It had to be removed with a strong detergent shampoo, because it clogged the hair follicles. The shampoo stripped the hair, undoing any good the oil might have done it, and irritated the scalp into the bargain. Hair-loss and dandruff were often the results. Today's preparations are lighter and kinder to the hair and leave it looking clean and healthy.

Black hair should be washed as often as necessary with a mild shampoo. Always follow the shampoo with a conditioner, and give your hair a wax or oil deep-conditioning treatment every month or fortnight. For dry or irritated scalps there are special scalp conditioners. Moisturize your hair every day that you don't wash it, with one of the aerosol preparations available at your chemist. Because black hair is highly sensitive to atmospheric conditions it loses moisture rapidly when indoor or outdoor air is dry and hot, becoming progressively dull and dry. It will also absorb moisture in damp or humid conditions, thereby losing its style — you may find a reversion-resistant hair spray a help. This will both hold your style and prevent excessive loss of moisture.

Get your hair trimmed regularly. Black hair is wayward and needs constant taming as well as pampering. Many black women who don't like the limitations of the frizzy halo now sculpt their hair in a spectacular design of head-plaits. This can be a most individual expression of your personality — the height of elegance, intricately coiled and corn-rowed, or a simple fringe of tiny plaits framing your face.

Another way to tame black hair is to straighten it. If you are wary of damaging fragile hair with a chemical straightener you can use a hot comb or curling tongs. The hair will need to be well conditioned before heat is applied. After washing, divide your hair into five sections — top, two sides, crown and nape. Twist and pin up each section out of the way. Beginning at the nape, apply concentrated scalp and hair conditioner. Comb a layer of the hair downwards, rub the conditioner into the scalp with the fingertips, and comb it right through the hair, paying special attention to the ends. Gradually move round the sides and front of the

A way to keep black hair looking neat is to use braiding, corn rowing or coiling, or, as here, where the style has been finished with decorative beaded ends and fringe.

26

An elegant and superbly conditioned style where the hair has been conditioned, covered with tiny plaits, piled on top of the head and, using a tail comb, sculpted into a dramatic asymetrical look.

head, finishing with the crown. The process will take time, but the end result — glossy, well-protected hair — is well worth the effort.

Once the whole head has been conditioned, you can begin to go over the hair again, smoothing it out with the curling tongs or hot comb. Always use an appliance that is thermostatically controlled. When you have worked through each section, and all the hair is straight, curl the hair into style on large rollers or with the curling tongs. (For information on chemical straightening and a new, soft, curly perm for black hair, *see* the section on perming and straightening.)

If you want to colour your hair, you should seek the advice of a professional hairdresser. It is difficult to colour very curly hair yourself and harsh chemicals are not kind to dry, brittle hair or sensitive scalps. A semi-permanent rinse in a rich chestnut or deep brown can add depth and glow to your hair colour, and spray-on highlights and glitter look stunning for a temporary change of mood.

A flattering hairstyle can be the most important single factor in your appearance. Not only does it tell about your character, it balances your body, frames your face and complements your clothes. A really professional haircut is a valuable investment, because it will make you feel good as well as look good.

When choosing a new hairstyle you should look carefully at the shape of your face. Try this when shampooing your hair. Lather it up on to the top of your head, put your glasses on if you wear them, and pull and pat it into different shapes. View the result in a long mirror as well as the one in your bathroom.

- If you have an oval face, you are very lucky. Any style will suit you.

- A long face is best complemented by short hair that is quite full, with a fringe. Don't go for a severe, long hairdo that will only accentuate the length of your face.

- If you have a round face, you should aim to add length. If you don't want long hair, part your hair on the side or add fullness on top. Avoid a neat bob with a fringe.

- All a square face needs is a little softening if the jawline is too heavy. Draw the attention away from the jaw with a diagonal fringe, soft tendrils of hair falling forward from the hairline and around the ears if you wear your hair up, or long loose hair with a bit of bounce below chin level.

Choosing a Hairstyle

● A heart-shaped face is also easy to flatter. All you need to do is avoid a heavy slab of fringe that will make your face into a triangle. A softer fringe will help.

● Try a soft fringe, too, for a high forehead, or a very heavy fringe that starts quite a way back and is 'V'-shaped, with the point of the 'V' in the centre behind your forehead.

● If you have a receding or double chin, you need to draw attention away from it. Your hair will look best either piled to the top and back of your head, to balance the chin, or hanging loose to hide it.

● A large nose needs a short, fluffy style; anything sleek or straight will only emphasize it.

Once you have decided on the style that will suit your face, you need to look at your hair type to see whether the requirements of the one fit the potential of the other. Your hair may be thick or fine, curly or straight, and these factors will determine to a certain extent what you can do with it.

If you have thick or curly hair, you have plenty of natural volume to play with. Fine straight hair needs to be long, or permed, before you can achieve much volume — the sleek look is what comes naturally to it. However, the success of your hairstyle depends on the cut, and this can do much to offset any problems you may have with the nature of your particular hair.

Choosing a Hairdresser

A really good hairdresser is not only an expert stylist. He or she will listen carefully to you, the client, and will find out about your lifestyle — whether, for instance, you travel regularly to hot or humid climates or have the leisure to achieve a complicated hairstyle. Above all, he will look closely at your hair type and condition and advise you on both its potential and its limitations. A top hairdresser whose work you have admired in magazine photographs is not necessarily going to be the right one for you. It may not suit you to have the latest and most outrageous style that he has devised for a publicity shot. What you need is personal attention. A good hairdresser is one who will listen to your idea of how you want to look, study photographs of styles you like and then explain how a style would look on you and suggest modifications if necessary. An attentive hairdresser will try to dissuade you from a drastic and expensive change of style or colour that would be wrong for your hair type and which you might come to regret.

Take your time in settling down with a new hairdresser. A recommendation from a friend may encourage you to visit a new salon, where you

Choosing a Hairdresser

All these pictures show the same girl with a different hairstyle, from the romantic to the sophisticated, emphasising how important a hairdresser is in reflecting an image or personality.

can test the waters by having nothing more than a trim and blow-dry. Don't attempt to change your style on the first visit. Wait until you're sure that you like the hairdresser's work. A visit to the salon should be a treat, not a chore. Choose somewhere with an atmosphere you like, where the staff are friendly and where the decor and music, if there is any, suit your mood. You want to be relaxed and you want to strike up a rapport with your hairdresser, even if conversation is minimal; otherwise you won't come out looking and feeling your best. It's important that you be punctual — you don't want your stylist to take revenge on your hair — and that if you're kept waiting you get an apology for the delay. Make sure, too, that you choose somewhere where brushes, towels and overalls are absolutely clean. There's nothing less appetizing than someone else's dirty comb.

If you have enjoyed your first visit and you look and feel good, you may well have found a winner. Go back for a trim, and perhaps a deep-conditioning treatment once a month, until you feel confident that your hairdresser understands you and your hair. Only after this trial period should you change your style. Then you'll be looking forward to the results, not dreading them. Once you have found the salon of your choice try not to rely on just the one stylist. Good looking hair depends on regular care and attention and regular cutting. if more than one person knows you and how you like your hair you won't be stuck if one or other of them goes on holiday, has a day off or suddenly decides to leave.

There are three types of hair colour: temporary, semi-permanent and permanent.

Temporary colour

The mildest colourant you can use is the water rinse. This adds colour to the outer layer of the hair, the cuticle, which is then washed away with the next shampoo. It will also come off, of course, if you go out in the rain. Water rinses are useful to tone streaks of grey hair or to soften a too-brassy blond. A skin test is seldom needed for water rinses. They are simple to use at home and are usually applied after shampooing. The same effects can be achieved with coloured setting lotions, all-in-one shampoo/rinses, coloured sprays and gels or mousses.

Semi-permanent colour

Semi-permanents contain no bleaching agents and so cannot lighten the hair. They merely change its tone. The colour does penetrate the cuticle temporarily, but is washed out after about half a dozen shampoos. A semi-permanent tint is useful for disguising grey hairs, giving depth to mousy hair and life to a dull blonde, or enriching brown hair with reddish tones. If you tint your hair at home, you will need to carry out a skin test 24 hours before you use the product on your hair. If you follow the manufacturer's instructions closely, you will give your hair added lustre, because most semi-permanent tints contain an effective conditioner.

Permanent colour

Choose a tint that's only two or three shades lighter than your own colour. A strand test will help you decide if you've made the right choice. Follow the manufacturer's instructions and study the results in the sunlight. If you like what you see, hold the strand to your face and check that it doesn't clash with your complexion. A hairdresser will also do a skin test—usually behind your ear where it will not show up—to see if your skin reacts with the dye. You should also do a skin test when colouring hair at home. It should be done every time and also if you change products—or colour—as each one will contain different chemicals.

Colouring Your Hair

Permanent tinting is a chemical process through which a bleaching agent strips the hair of its natural colour and makes it more porous so that it reacts with and absorbs the new colour. Timing is crucial, and a professional colourist will be able to judge how long to leave the colour on your particular hair type, (fine hair takes less time to absorb the colour than coarser hair).

Permanent tinting can go badly wrong, resulting in a surprising colour and damaged hair, if it is not done properly. If you choose to do it at home, make sure to follow the manufacturer's instructions exactly. Misuse of bleaching or permanent colouring may cause your hair to split and break.

Highlighting, streaking and tipping

These are sophisticated and selective forms of permanent colouring that require expert timing and blending. Nowadays they can be carried out at home. Professional highlighting is popular, though expensive, because it emphasizes the nuances of colour in your hair, underlining its natural beauty. Strands of hair are drawn through holes in a plastic cap and treated with bleach or woven out and then wrapped in tin foil. The bleaching agent is rinsed off when the desired colour has been reached, and the whole head is then shampooed and conditioned, perhaps after having been treated with a semi-permanent toner to blend the shades more subtly. Highlights grow out fairly naturally and need to be renewed only every three or four months.

Vegetables dyes

Unlike many synthetic dyes most vegetable dyes do not alter the structure of your hair. A skin test should be done when using vegetable dyes, to check there is no irritation. These dyes cling to the cuticle of the hair and leave it soft and full of body. The most popular vegetable dye is henna, used for thousands of years to give rich, red tones. Henna is the dried, crushed leaves of the Lawsonia plant. It is mixed with hot water and a dash of lemon juice of vinegar and, for the most even results, painted on to the

Subtle use of highlights (opposite) can enliven a blonde. Above: a short cut is given added interest with a strikingly original permanent tint. Above right: the colour of another short spiky cut is reinforced by use of dark shade such as the dramatic blue-black used here.

Colouring Your Hair

hair section by section. If you do this at home you will make a mess: wear old clothes and be prepared to spend some time cleaning your bathroom afterwards. Pile the hennaed hair on top of your head, cleaning any henna off your skin with damp cotton wool (pay attention to the ears, too). Wrap a strip of cotton wool around the hairline to stop the dye from running down your face and cover the head in cling film. Tie an old scarf or towel round your head. To speed up the colouring process, warm your head by using a hairdryer or sitting in the sun. When you decide your time is up, wash out the henna with several shampooings and rinse thoroughly. Your hair will be left in top condition, full and lustrous. Some henna products may not be pure henna and are compounded with metallic salts or synthetic dyes to make them act more quickly; those may not be compatible with other forms of permanent hair colour or perm. To test the colour, do a strand test, although the instruction leaflets that come with most brands of true red henna usually err on the cautious side where timing is concerned. Don't use henna on blonde, grey, white or chemically tinted hair, as the results will be unpredictable.

Other natural dyes can be made from infusions of camomile or marigold, both of which produce a subtle, lightening effect, or from sage or walnut, which will give a soft, brown tone to grey hair.

~PAINT HAIR~ ~PILE HAIR UP~ CLEAN SKIN ~WRAP COTTONWOOL ROUND HEAD~ ~TIE TOWEL ON HEAD~ ~IN SECTIONS~ ~WITH DAMP COTTONWOOL~ ~COVER IN CLINGFILM~ ~USE HAIRDRYER~

Soft and regular corkscrew curls create a dramatic look.

Perming

Today's perms aim not for a rigid, waffle-iron effect, but for softness, bounce, volume and movement. They are especially useful for fine, straight hair that lacks body. If you covet a tight curl you can still have it, but without dryness, frizz and breaking hairs. There is also a new curly perm for black hair that brings softness and regularity to wayward and wiry curls. The perm is a two-stage process. The first lotion applied is a chemical that softens the structure of the hair; this is then rinsed away very thoroughly and the second lotion is applied. This is a neutralizer that sets the hair into the new position determined by the curling rods. A final rinse and the perm is complete. Modern perms, used properly, should leave your hair shining and lustrous, but perming is nevertheless a chemical process that alters the structure of the hair and is therefore potentially damaging to it.

You should not perm damaged hair. Don't perm and tint within the same two weeks, and don't perm if you have an irritated scalp. Always use a conditioner each time you wash permed hair. Avoid brushing if possible, as this will pull out the curl. If you have a wash-and-wear curly style, try to let your hair dry naturally and run your fingers through it as it dries for a soft, bouncy look. Use a wide-toothed not a narrow-toothed, comb. If your hair looks a bit squashed after you've slept on it, spray with water from a plant spray and it will spring into shape.

Straightening

This is a similar but more drastic process, than perming. The structure of the hair is altered and the hairshaft is stretched before being set into a new shape. This is where the damage is likely to occur, because hair breaks very easily if it is stretched when wet. Because black hair is by nature brittle and porous, straightening should be carried out only in a salon. Remember that as new, curly hair grows, the straightened hair will look less natural.

HANDS & FEET

Hands and feet, our hardworking extremities, are often overlooked by people who are otherwise quite thorough in their bodycare. They deserve better treatment.

Hands

Hands reveal a lot about a person's character and health. Palmists say they tell the story of your life. The skin on our hands gets exposed to harsher treatment than that on other parts of the body. Hands are subjected to extremes of temperature, harsh detergents and constant immersion in water, with resulting dehydration. If you do not look after them properly they can age very quickly, the skin on the backs of the hands becomes loose and liver-spotted. Nails are a focus of attention and need special care to keep them healthy and in good condition.

Protect your hands from the elements whenever you can. Wear gloves in cold weather to prevent chapping and wear rubber gloves or barrier cream against hot water or hard work. Always dry your hands thoroughly after washing and rub them well with handcream. Soak rough hands in warm olive oil or petroleum jelly — blot off when cool. Use a sun screen on the backs of your hands in summer — it is the ultraviolet rays of the sun which cause the concentrations of melanin in the skin known as liver spots. Use a nailbrush and pumice stone on really dirty hands, bleach away stains with lemon juice and massage round the nails with cuticle cream.

Nails

A healthy diet will show in your nails, which should be rosy and lustrous, firm and strong. Poor nails are sometimes the result of a diet deficient in vitamins, zinc or iron. Or they are the result of neglect or, more often, the use of nail polish and remover, which can cause dryness and discolouration. The vitamin A in cod liver oil and carrot juice is good for splitting nails. Fingernails grow faster than toenails — about 1mm ($\frac{1}{25}$in) per week — and a weekly manicure will keep them in good shape. Make sure not to cut down the sides of the nails too far when trimming them.

Applying nail polish

There are a few key steps to follow when applying nail polish. Always apply a base coat to your nails first to protect them from staining. Let the base dry for five minutes. Roll the nail-polish between your palms rather than shaking it. This will warm the polish and make it flow more smoothly. Open the bottle and gather enough polish on the brush for three strokes. Apply the first to the centre of the nail from base to tip; the other two to the sides. Allow to dry for 10 minutes, then apply a second coat. After a further 10 minutes apply a sealer to your nails and allow to dry for about half an hour.

Manicure

1 Remove all traces of old polish with an oil-based remover on cotton wool or a tissue. Do not soak your nails before filing, as this will soften them.

2 File each nail with an emery board by gently stroking from the side to the centre; do not file back and forth.

3 Rub cuticle cream or petroleum jelly into the cuticles and apply moisturizing cream to the nails and hands.

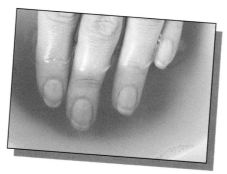

4 Soak your fingernails for five minutes in a small bowl of warmed baby oil.

5 With a soft toothbrush, brush under your nails so that they are completely clean. Rinse your hands in warm water and dry thoroughly.

6 Push your cuticles back with your fingertips.

7 Repeat with an orange stick. Never cut your cuticles.

8 Rinse your hands again in warm water. Your manicure is now complete. If you are going to apply nail polish, wait for five minutes. Remove any traces of excess creams or oils with nail varnish remover.

Aching feet can infect the whole body with misery, but most foot problems are self-inflicted and boil down to wearing uncomfortable or ill-fitting shoes. The average pair of feet walks 70,000 miles in a lifetime and city-dwellers can cover about 10 miles a day. By the time they reach adulthood, most people have managed to distort the natural shape of their feet by wearing the wrong shoes, so that they spend the rest of their lives walking in a manner designed to compensate for these deformities, however slight.

The choice of a good pair of shoes is obviously very important. There should be enough toe-room and the feet should not be cramped at any point. It is no good hoping that a shoe will loosen up and mould itself to your foot in time — it won't. There should not be too much room at the back of the shoe or it will rub as you walk. High heels are not good for the feet or legs. Flat shoes are best, but if you like wearing heels, restrict the height to 3cm (1-1½in). Really high heels cause the weight of the body to be forced onto the toes, which get crushed. The ankles also take extra strain in attempting to balance on wobbly heels. The calf muscles are tensed and the posture altered, which could mean backache.

Go barefoot as often as you can and try to avoid standing still for long periods. Standing exacerbates varicose veins, as do tight boots or pop sox. Brisk walking, running, dancing and swimming are all good exercises for the legs and feet.

For tired feet paddling in cold water or walking on dewy grass is strongly recommended. Or give yourself a foot-bath with a cup of salt in a basin of warm water. Relax with your feet in the water and then douse them briefly in cold water, before drying thoroughly. Put on warm woolly socks and lie back with your feet above your head.

Wash your feet every day and put on fresh socks or stockings. Use a pumice stone on hard skin, corns and callouses after a long soak to soften them. Keeping your feet clean and dry will guard against athlete's foot. Should you suffer from this infection, treat between the toes with fungicidal cream and powder and put on cotton socks before going to bed. If your feet sweat a lot, rub them with surgical spirit after washing, then dust with talcum powder. Wear socks and shoes made of non-synthetic materials. Regular visits to a chiropodist will keep your feet in trim, and they become a necessity if you have chilblains, bunions or verrucas (warts). Chilblains are caused by bad circulation. Exercises and keeping your feet warm can help. Bunions sometimes run in families, but they are usually caused by ill-fitting shoes.

Pedicure

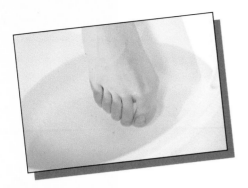

1 Wash each foot in turn in warm soapy water.

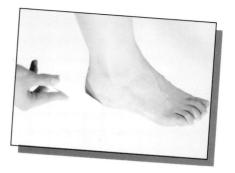

2 Gently rub the soles and heels with a pumice stone to remove hard skin.

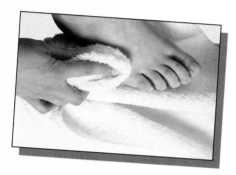

3 Dry the feet thoroughly, especially between the toes.

4 Trim the nails with a nailclipper or scissors, cutting them straight across. Do not cut down the sides of the nails.

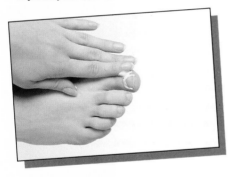

5 Rub petroleum jelly or cuticle cream into the sides and base of the nails with your fingertips.

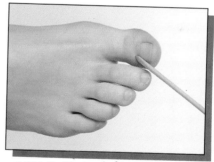

6 With the blunt end of an orange stick, work at the sides and base of the nails to ease the skin back.

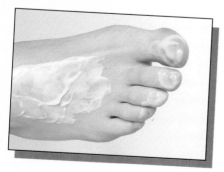

7 Rub the feet and nails all over with hand or body cream.

8 To round off the pedicure, apply nail polish. First apply a base coat, then two coats of polish, allowing plenty of time to dry in between coats.

EATING

43

Ideas about healthy eating have changed dramatically over the last couple of decades. People used to be worried that they were not getting enough protein; now they are worried that they are eating too much. Today's diet for health is low in protein and fat and high in fibre. Sugar is off the menu and so are refined carbohydrates. Salt is out. Coffee and alcohol are to be taken only in moderation.

For a healthy body you should eat plenty of fresh fruit and vegetables, as much as possible in their raw state. Wholegrains are important. This means wholewheat bread, brown rice and wholewheat pasta. Replace animal protein with vegetable protein wherever possible, eating plenty of beans, peas and dried pulses. Cut down on meat, if you eat it, and don't eat the fat. Instead of butter, use polyunsaturated margarine. Instead of full-fat cheese, choose cottage cheese. Low-fat yoghurt is very good for the digestion. Replace coffee with herbal tea, sweetened perhaps with honey; drink at least a pint of mineral water a day. Avoid cakes, sweets, desserts made with sugar and cream and sweetened drinks.

Fibre is indigestible, and this is precisely why you should eat it. It is moved quickly through the digestive tract, so that regular consumption of fibre means regular bowel movements. The body is thus regularly cleared of waste. Constipation is a terrible thing to suffer from. It means bad breath, bad skin, lifeless hair, a general feeling of discomfort and dullness and, more seriously, a predisposition towards diseases of the bowel such as cancer, diseases virtually unknown in countries that have stuck to a relatively 'primitive' diet. All this can be changed by eating fibre, present to a high degree in beans and bran as well as in fruit, other vegetables and wholegrains.

In the 1870s roller mills came into action, making stone milling of flour pretty well obsolete. Roller milling was efficient and fast. It produced white flour cheaply, a refined product that only the rich had been able to afford up to then. It also produced the by-products, chaff (bran) and wheatgerm, which could be sold as animal feed. No one had to eat coarse, dark bread any longer instead of light, white loaves and cakes. What they ate was starch, while the animals got the roughage, the protein and the vitamin E contained in wheatgerm. We know now, however, that the animals were being fed the best part of the grain and that the process of 'refinement' had backfired drastically.

Fibre is important for slimming as well as for health, and this is the reason for the success of Audrey Eyton's F-Plan Diet. High-fibre foods are bulky and therefore satisfying to the appetite as well as being relatively low in calories. Beans and wholegrains are also rich in proteins, while fruit and vegetables contain essential vitamins, minerals and trace elements. So high-fibre foods satisfy the appetite and meet nutritional requirements without overburdening the body with calories. People who do not eat enough fibre are likely to consume larger quantities of high-calorie, high-protein foods that move sluggishly through the gut.

In short, a high-fibre diet really does work. And the best thing about it is that you can make it a way of life, so that you stay slim once you have lost the excess weight.

The changing images of woman: above; a celebration of fecundity in the 30,000-year-old Venus from Willendorf which dates from paleolithic times. Below, dressed in the flapper-style of the period actress Colleen Moore dances before a roomful of admirers in a scene from an early 30s movie.

Slimming

In many parts of the world, and indeed in the West until the 1920s, fat has been desirable. If food is scarce, threatening illness and starvation, then thinness is naturally equated with disease and poverty. It follows that a person who can afford to be sleek and fat is rich, and fat becomes a status symbol.

From earliest times, fat has been beautiful. The Venus from Willendorf is a 30,000-year-old sculpture — one of the oldest surviving works of art in the world — and it portrays a plump lady from the paleolithic period of the type Rubens would have admired. A hundred years ago in Uganda nubile girls were confined to 'fattening tents', where they were fed on a diet of milk until they became so fat that they could hardly walk. In this heightened state of attractiveness they were presented to their bridegrooms.

Fat people represent a desirable elite in a world where malnutrition is the norm. But as eating improves, so thinness becomes more attractive. Once fat is accessible to all, indeed it becomes difficult to avoid, everyone wants to be thin. The ideal weight, whether heavy or light, is still associated with wealth. The Duchess of Windsor once made a remark for which she became famous: 'For a woman it is impossible to be too thin or too rich.' A woman's weight is perceived to be an indication of her worth, just as much today as ever. In times of shortage they must strive to be fat; in times of glut they must aspire to be lean.

After 1960 even *Playboy* models and beauty queens got thinner. Every year during the 1960s the new Miss America weighed in at $\frac{1}{2}$lb less than her predecessor. Over the same period the weight of the average American woman increased by the same amount, so that the discrepancy beween the real and the ideal increased every year. Not surprisingly, the slimming business really began to take off. It has continued to boom. It has been found that at any one time 60 per cent of American women are on a diet and that one in four has at one time enrolled in a weight-loss programme. Sales of books, magazines, slimming gadgets and diet foods prove that there is a lot of money to be made out of women's obsessions with their weight.

There is, of course, no doubt that to be overweight is bad for the health. It carries an increased risk of diabetes, gall bladder disease, high blood-pressure and cancer. A lot of extra weight in a pot belly puts a strain on the heart. In addition, overweight people are more at risk during surgery or pregnancy. On the other hand, it is no healthier to be very thin than it is to be obese. Many of the women who diet are not obese, but only mildly overweight.

The only way to lose weight permanently is to change one's eating habits . A healthy diet is described at the beginning of this

The 50s actress Marilyn Monroe with the sexy blonde hair, highly glossed pouting lips and waist-nipped lurex dress that symbolised glamour to the men of a generation and whose style was emulated by many women.

chapter. Concentrate on every mouthful of food, chewing slowly. This will make you more aware of the food you are eating and you will enjoy it more. Don't eat while watching television. Not only will this divert your attention from your food, but it will also mean that you will feel hungry every time you turn the television on. Reduce your contact with food to a minimum, so that you avoid temptation. Take a portion of food and put the rest away so that you don't take a second helping without realizing what you are doing. Always keep food in covered containers so that you don't catch sight of it by accident. Don't snack between meals. Eating should be a controlled activity that occurs at set times, not a continuous activity that spills all over your day. Once you have got it thoroughly under control, eating sensibly will become second nature to you.

Anorexia

Anorexia nervosa is a disease that chiefly (but not exclusively) affects adolescent girls. It begins with an obsessive need to go on a diet. An anorexic will lose weight dramatically, then not be able to stop dieting. Though very thin, even emaciated, she will persist in believing herself to be overweight. She will take pride in the fact that she can exercise such control over her body as to continually deny herself food. She may also indulge in violent exercise in an effort to reduce her weight still further. Anorexia sufferers need specialist help, as they often refuse all inducement to eat and get well again.

Bulimia nervosa is a related complaint that involves going on binges, followed by vomiting. An anorexic can also suffer from bulimia, although bulimics are not necessarily overweight. A bulimic will plan a binge as a means of combatting stress or depression. She will buy a large quantity of high-calorie food, probably a 'forbidden' food such as ice cream or cake, and eat it rapidly, in private, without enjoyment. Feelings of guilt and nausea result and the sufferer forces herself to vomit. Though at first she finds this as unpleasant as anyone else would, it gradually becomes easier until it reaches the point of being an almost involuntary reaction. Bulimics, too, need specialist treatment. The presence of the disease is more difficult to detect than anorexia, the symptoms of which are more obvious.

EXERCISE

The point of exercising is to keep the body in good working order so that it will last longer. Exercise keeps the muscles firm and strong and makes the heart pump blood more efficiently round the body. The lungs expand fully, drawing in more oxygen. The arteries are enlarged and strengthened. Blood-pressure goes down, as does the concentration of blood fats. Adrenalin, built up by stress, is dispersed. Not only does exercise reduce the risk of a heart attack, it makes you physically and mentally alert and improves your ability to relax. It gives an added self-confidence that comes from a knowledge of the body. In short, exercise is good for you.

But it is good for you only if you enjoy it. Punishing forms of exercise, intended to thrash the reluctant body into fitness, won't succeed if they make you miserable. The best exercise is regular, rhythmic exercise at a pace you can stand. If unfit, begin gently, not expecting too much of yourself, and gradually build up your strength and energy until you can push yourself a little harder and enjoy it.

Aerobic exercises — those that involve processing oxygen efficiently through the body, such as running, rowing, swimming and cycling — are much better for body maintenance than anaerobic exercises, which involve very vigorous bursts of activity that will leave you exhausted. Anaerobic exercises are sports such as squash, tennis and sprinting. The kind of exercise that is best for overall fitness involves a sustained effort, keeping up a certain pace over a longish period. And aerobic exercises are the best possible training if you want to succeed at anaerobic sports.

Other forms of exercise include ballet and yoga and involve graceful and rhythmic movements that develop the suppleness of the body, the tone of the muscles and the lubrication of the joints.

Yoga stretches and tones the body, improving the functioning of muscles and joints. The spine becomes more flexible and the exercises also work on the internal organs, the glands and the nerves. Yoga has been practised in India for thousands of years and is the world's most ancient system of personal development. The word 'yoga' means 'joining' — the joining of the self to Brahman, the unchanging reality. Personal preconceptions and the clutter of everyday life are shed in a purification of mind and body which gives freedom from time and space.

One of the most important things about yoga is that it enables you to relax. It is possible to be tense all the time and not known it — even to lie rigidly in bed, grimly awaiting sleep, without realizing that mind and body are merely galvanized for the sound of the alarm clock and the next headlong rush into action. Try consciously tensing and relaxing your muscles to see just how keyed up you are.

The exercise of yoga consists of getting into and out of a series of postures — asanas. Movements are slow and graceful, never jerky. They extend your reach gradually and should never be forced. After a session of yoga you should feel both relaxed and full of energy, not exhausted and strained. Breathing is important to help you move correctly.

In performing the following sequence of 12 asanas, don't worry if you can't get into some of the positions at first. You will be able to in time. Imagine yourself forming the shapes described by the illustrations even if you can't achieve them.

The Sun Salutation

This series of 12 asanas is traditionally performed at dawn, as a greeting to the sun. It forms a gentle warming-up exercise from which you can go on to other yoga asanas. Alternatively, you can practise the cycle several times a day, to stretch the muscles and bring flexibility to the spine. It will also trim the waist.

1 Stand with your back straight and feet together. Press your palms together in the prayer position. Feel balanced. Exhale.

2 Inhale and stretch up your arms, arching your back from the waist and pressing your hips forward. Keep your legs straight and let your neck relax.

The Sun Salutation

3 *Exhale and bring your body forward and down so that your hands touch the floor. In time you should be able to press your palms flat alongside your feet.*

4 *Inhale and push one leg out behind you, touching the floor with the balls of your toes and your knee. Stretch your leg and arch your back. Lift your chin to form a continuous curve.*

5 *Holding your breath, stretch the second leg back to join the first. Raise yourself up on hands and feet. Keep your body in a straight line, looking down between your hands.*

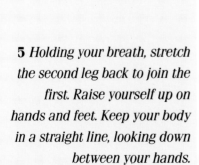

The Sun Salutation

6 *Exhale, lowering yourself to the ground — first the knees, then the chest, then the forehead. Keep your toes curled and your hips raised.*

7 *Inhale, lowering your hips to the ground and raising your torso. Point your toes and completely arch your back.*

8 *Exhale, raising the hips, curling your toes under and bending head inwards. Be conscious of making a regular inverted 'V' shape.*

The Sun Salutation

9 *Inhale, stepping forward with one foot between your palms. This position is the mirror of that held in step 4.*

10 *Exhale, bringing the second leg forward to join the first, as in step 3.*

11 *Inhale, lifting your torso up and stretching your arms forward, then back over your head. Arch your back, relax your neck and push your hips forward as in step 2.*

12 *Exhale, returning to an upright position. Let your arms fall gently by your sides.*

EXERCISE

Massage — rhythmically stroking and touching another person to bring relaxation and comfort — is the oldest and simplest form of therapy. It relieves nervous tension and relaxes knotted muscles, improving circulation and body tone and induces a feeling of well-being and wholeness. Massage is a wordless communication between two people and expresses care and understanding. It can be as beneficial for the giver as for the receiver, if both parties concentrate themselves solely on the point of contact.

Touch is recognition and acceptance and vitally necessary for the development of self-awareness. Babies deprived of hugging and cuddling show symptoms of undernourishment. Western behavioural patterns allow for only the most perfunctory social touching between adults — men shake hands of slap each other's backs and women brush cheeks. Outside of sexual relationships our bodies are isolated from others. Massage is a way of getting back in touch.

The requirements for massage are simple. You will need a warm, quiet room, free of draughts and intrusions such as the radio or telephone. The atmosphere should be relaxing, the lights dim. Perhaps the best place for a massage is in front of a flickering fire. Ideally the receiver should be naked, but if this causes discomfort, then the giver can work around the clothes that are left on. The giver should wear comfortable loose-fitting garments that will not restrict movement. The receiver should lie on a firm surface, such as the floor or a table. It is essential that he or she should be made comfortable with rugs and cushions or pillows. Drape a towel over these and use another towel to cover the parts of the body that you are not working on if you wish. The receiver should remove any jewellery that might get in the way and contact lenses, too.

The giver should remove jewellery, especially rings. Nails should be short and not sharp. Wash your hands before giving the massage. Explain to your partner how you are intending to work. Surprises are not relaxing. Do not massage the following areas: scars of recent surgery, broken skin, varicose veins, bruises, lumps or swellings, itchy places, warts or the belly of a woman in the first three months of pregnancy. Do not massage anyone with arthritis — get the advice of your doctor. Ask the receiver to tell you about any problems. Encourage him or her to tell you when anything feels particularly good or if something is uncomfortable. Otherwise do not talk, since to do so will ruin your mutual concentration.

The laying-on of hands is an ancient form of healing, regarded with some awe. But everyone has the power to give, and the more you are aware of it, the better you will be able to transmit it. Begin by centring yourself. The Japanese have a word, *hara*, which means lower abdomen. This is the centre of the body, from which power flows. Focus yourself on this centre and allow the feeling to spread through your body and arms to your fingertips. Relax your hands and wrists by shaking them. While you are massaging your partner, keep your back straight and move from your pelvis. Always keep yourself aware of the power in your hands.

Make sure that you are sitting, kneeling or standing in a comfortable and balanced position; any awkwardness or tension will transmit itself straight to your partner. Do not attemp to massage if you are angry or upset. The object of massage is to share positive, not negative, feelings.

As a lubricant you will need a massage oil. This will enable your hands to move smoothly over the receiver's body without friction. The most luxurious oils are those containing plant essences used in aromatherapy (*see* p.80). However, you can use almond oil, baby oil or vegetable oil, whichever you have to hand. Keep the oil close to you (you will not need a lot of it), but make sure to put it somewhere where you will not knock it over. Warm the oil before use by rubbing it between your hands; never drip it directly onto your partner's body.

Massage Strokes

Massage should always begin with the lightest touch, gradually increasing concentration and pressure until you reach below the soft flesh and the superficial muscles to massage the joints. Then relax, ending as gently as you began. Some practitioners advocate maintaining constant contact until the massage is over, but as long as you break and re-establish contact with the lightest of touches this should not be necessary. The advantages of breaking contact is that you can move round easily to the next position and rub more oil on your hands when necessary.

There are four basic massage strokes, described below in ascending order of pressure applied.

● Light strokes should be used to begin and end the massage and to move from one part of the body to another. These strokes are broad, fluent and soothing, reminiscent of water flowing smoothly over the flesh. Mould your palms and fingers into the contours of your partner's body as your hands glide effortlessly across it.

● Begin to work more deeply and more specifically, pulling and kneading rhythmically, one hand echoing the movement of the other. Stretch the flesh under your hands, then let it relax. Don't grab, but keep your hands on the body, rocking back on the heel of the hand between movements.

● Progress to really penetrating strokes, working concentratedly with the ball of the thumb, fingertips and the heel of the hand. Push rhythmically, describing tiny circles. Use your body weight. Be as firm as you can without hurting.

● A fourth type of stroke can be added if the mood is right. This is percussion. It is vigorous and stimulating, rather than relaxing, and you should find out beforehand if it will be welcome. Brisk strokes including hacking, a rhythmic chopping movement with the side of the hands, pummelling with the side of the fists (keep it bouncy, avoiding the force of a punch), and vigorous plucking with the fingertips.

The Back

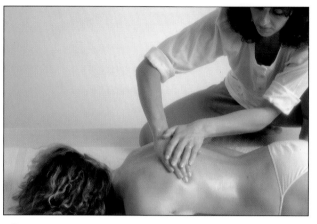

1 To begin the massage, pour a little oil into the palms of your hands, sit alongside your partner and start on the side of the body opposite you. Work from the small of the back, massaging in large circles down the side and up to the shoulder blades.

2 Work around the shoulder blade with the whole hand, pushing away from the spine with firm strokes. Repeat several times.

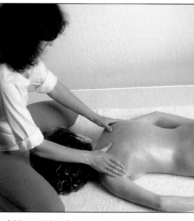

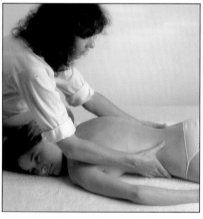

3 With your fingertips pull the muscle towards you and with the flat of your hand circle under the shoulder blade. Repeat several times. Repeat the sequence on your partner's other side.

4 Move behind your partner's head and with thumbs on either side of the spine (not on the spine, on the muscle), work down towards the buttocks with small circular movements.

5 Work up the sides from the hips to the shoulders with the flat of the hand in firm strokes. Repeat several times.

6 Smooth down the back with the flat of the hand, being careful to avoid the spine.

7 Smooth down the arms in the same way. Repeat steps 6 and 7 several times.

8 To finish the back massage, sit next to your partner and smooth the back firmly and lightly all over several times.

Backs of Legs and Feet

  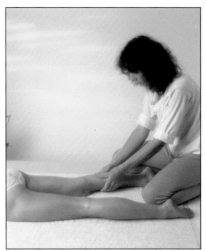

1 Place both hands on your partner's thigh. Use your thumbs to massage down the leg in small, outward circles from the thigh down to the ankle, working on all the muscles as you go.

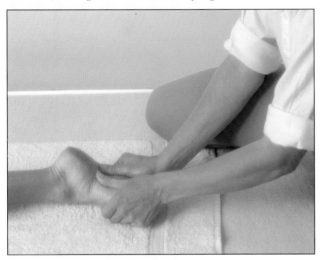 

2 Continue on the foot describing small, outward, spiralling circles.

3 Bend the leg at the knee joint and stretch the foot carefully upwards. Repeat.

4 Rotate the ankle slowly and gently, first clockwise, then anticlockwise.

5 Gently lift the leg and move slowly from side to side. Never force the leg. Stop if there is any pain.

6 Put the leg down and finish with long, firm strokes down the whole leg. Repeat the whole sequence with the other leg.

Arms and Hands

1 Sit next to your partner, here a child, and hold the hand nearest to you.

2 Massage with the thumb on the muscle between the shoulder and the neck.

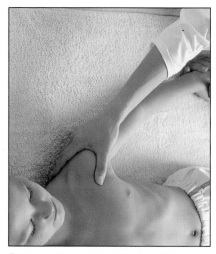

3 Move on to the joint at the top of the arm and work it with your thumb.

4 Work down the arm with the thumb all the way to the hand. Repeat.

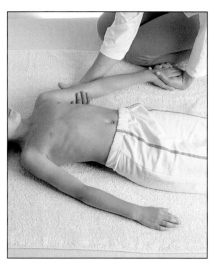

5 Repeat down the back of the arm to the hand with the same circular movement of the thumb. Repeat several times.

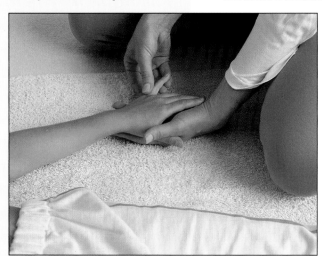

6 Massage the hand and the fingers with tiny, circular thumb movements. Gently stretch and rotate the fingers, first one way and then the other.

7 Finish with long, firm strokes from the shoulders to the fingers. Repeat several times. Move to your partner's other side and repeat the whole sequence on the other arm.

MASSAGE

Chest and Abdomen

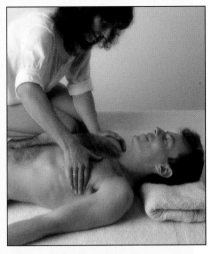

1 Massage the chest muscles below the collar bone with the thumb.

2 Circulate with the flat of the hand round the breast and rib area.

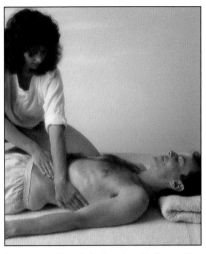

3 Using the flat of the hand, pull diagonally across the abdomen.

4 Alternate hands and repeat several times. Repeat the sequence on the other side of your partner's body. Then return to the right side.

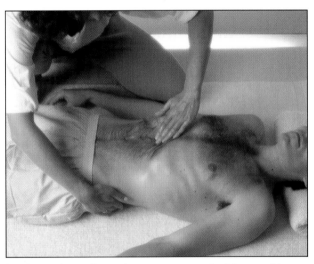

5 Make gentle circular strokes on your partner's abdomen with your fingertips. Always massage in a clockwise direction.

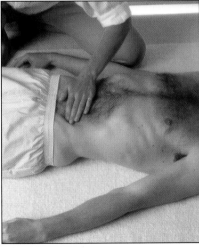

6 Repeat several times. Work your way around the stomach in a large circle.

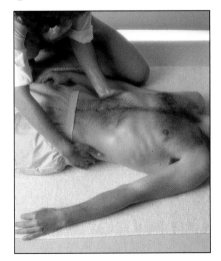

7 To finish, hold your partner's sides while he breathes in and out deeply. Repeat.

63

Front of Legs and Feet

1 With one hand support the back of your partner's knee. Using the thumb of the other hand, follow the contour of the thigh muscle in a diagonal direction from the inside of the knee to the hip. Repeat.

2 Work around the thigh muscle several times with your thumb in small, circular movements.

3 Massage down the outer edge of the thigh to the knee, with the hand behind the leg and the thumb rotating.

4 Support the knee and go up the inner thigh with the thumb rotating, then smooth downwards. Repeat several times.

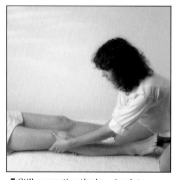

5 Still supporting the leg, circulate around the kneecap with the thumb. Repeat several times.

6 Massage down the calf muscle with circular thumb movements all the way down to the foot on both sides of the leg.

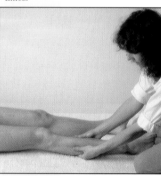

7 Using both thumbs, massage towards the foot with small circular movements.

8 Massage around the ankle bone with both hands, moving the fingertips in small circles.

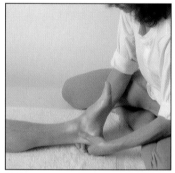

9 Massage the inner heel with rotating thumb movements on each side of the foot.

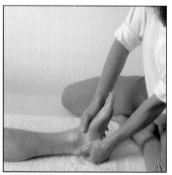

10 Massage the top of the foot with the heel of the hand, repeating the stroke several times.

11 Massage the sole of the foot with your thumb, working upwards towards the toes.

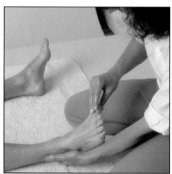

12 Stretch and massage the toes, rotating each gently.

Neck, Head and Face

1 Sit behind your partner's head and push the shoulders down gently, but firmly, with the heel of your hands.

2 Massage the shoulder joint with the thumbs, moving in an outward direction. Repeat several times.

3 Slightly turn your partner's head and support it with one hand. With your other hand massage the back of the neck. Repeat several times.

4 Gradually work up towards the crown of the head, moving in small circles. Cover half the head in this way, repeat the sequence on the other side.

5 Rest your hands gently, but firmly, on your partner's forehead and ask him or her to take deep breaths while your hands remain still.

6 Smooth your thumbs towards the centre of the forehead. Repeat several times.

7 Circulate your thumbs on the temples in small gentle movements.

8 Smooth downwards on the cheeks and stretch the skin upwards, ending the stroke at the temples.

9 Smooth the area between the upper lip and the nose up and outwards over the cheeks.

10 Smooth the chin upwards with the thumb and forefinger.

11 Smooth the skin upwards with the whole hand, working from the chin to the temples.

12 Massage the ears with the thumb and forefinger.

13 Gently, very slightly stretch the neck.

14 Rotate the head gently from side to side.

15 Finish by pulling gently through the hair.

HERBS

Herbs were used in ancient times to eat, and to stimulate the appetite, to ward off disease, cure the sick and heal wounds, to make perfumes and cosmetics, to dye cloth, to make holy oils and precious ointments and to embalm the dead. These uses are catalogued in the oldest surviving herbal, which was written 4000 years ago in Sumeria and which reveals a vast and detailed knowledge of the properties and potential of thousands of plants.

The Egyptians were the next to record their prescriptions, which they wrote down in the Ebers Papyrus of c.1550BC. At that time there were more than 2,000 herb doctors in Egypt, and their medicines included onions, myrrh, castor oil, caraway, poppy, pomegranates, dates, lotus, elder and mint.

In India the Hindu god, Siva — 'the first herbalist' — is often portrayed with a pot of herbs for health and healing in one hand and a lotus, for reproduction, in the other. On his head he wears a silver crescent to represent the moon, which rules over the earth's herbs. In ancient Greece, too, the healing power of herbs was deified in the figure of Aesculapius, the god of healing, who carried, among other things, a pineapple and a bunch of herbs.

The first famous doctor of ancient times was Hippocrates, who lived in Greece in the 5th century BC. He has become known as 'the father of modern medicine'. Like herbalists and practitioners of other branches of holistic medicine today, Hippocrates believed that a doctor should treat the patient rather than his disease. This belief is based on the view that illness is a manifestation of disharmony and imbalance in the patient's life, not a chance affliction that picks its victim at random. In prescribing treatment, the doctor should, on this view, take into account the patient's character, lifestyle, environment and diet, all of which, when examined, will help to indicate the root of the trouble to a trained and sympathetic observer.

In the first century AD the Greek scholar, Dioscorides, who is said to have been physician to Anthony and Cleopatra, travelled around Europe gathering and studying healing plants. He published his findings in *Materia Medica,* a herbal that remained unsurpassed for more than a thousand years and was current in the monasteries of medieval Europe. Dioscorides is the first known user of the drug, aspirin, which he made from the leaves of the white willow. Many ancient remedies, which must have been discovered by the often dangerous process of trial and error, are today being given the stamp of approval after investigation by modern pharmacological methods. Huge sums of money are being spent on research into rare and fast-disappearing plants in the South American rain forests, in the hope of finding cures for cancer, AIDS and other diseases before the plants are lost for ever.

It was the Romans who introduced herbalism into Britain. The conquerors brought with them the seeds of more than 2,000 plants, including parsley, sage, rosemary, thyme, fennel, borage and the huge, vicious stinging net-

Herbs

tles that today are still prevalent near the sites of former Roman encampments. The monasteries espoused herbalism as they did other branches of learning and the monks laid out physic gardens and constructed stills to extract the essential oils from the plants.

Herbalism is not an exact science and its principles are open to misinterpretation and abuse. Plants can be used to kill as well as cure and there are also those that cause paralysis and hallucinations. Some plants are more potent when gathered at night. It is no wonder that myths and legends have grown up about the power of plants and that they have been associated with witchcraft and black magic.

Culpeper, still famous today for the 'herbal' he wrote in 1653, was, ironically enough, responsible for bringing herbalism into disrepute in his day because of his strong belief in astrology. The Babylonians invented astrology and divided the heavens into the twelve signs of the Zodiac, each of which was said to have in its domain different colours, precious stones, plants and parts of the body. Naturally enough it was only a matter of time before astrology was used in conjunction with herbalism to diagnose illness and prescribe treatment — almost independently, of course, of the patient's true nature and needs. In the 16th century we read: 'Above all things next to grammar a physician must have his Astronomye, to know how, when and at what time every medicine ought to be administered.'

Culpeper was also heavily influenced by the 'Doctrine of Signatures'. This was a system of classifying plants and their healing properties according to their resemblance to various organs or aspects of the human body and to the environment in which they thrived. Thus, the lungwort *(pulmonaria)* gets its name from its spotted leaves. Because they look like lungs, it was assumed that the Creator had put his 'signature' on the plant to tell us that it would do the lungs good. In some cases this doctrine does, by chance, work. Willow bark *is* good for rheumatism — the doctrine of signatures explains this by saying that the willow grows in a damp place, and damp aggravates rheumatic disease. However, it is not true that all plants with red flowers purify the blood, nor that all plants with yellow flowers cure jaundice.

By Culpeper's day the herbalist's ancient authority was already being undermined, as people turned to the new, inorganic remedies being made by chemists. Synthetic medicines originated with the alchemist, Paracelsus (1493-1541), who distilled the essential oils of plants and combined them with other elements in his remedies. This is still the practice of the giant pharmaceutical companies today. To the herbalist, to extract some elements from a plant and discard others is to destroy the natural balance of its healing properties. Synthetic medicines work fast, sometimes effecting an about-turn in the patient's condition within days, or even hours. But they are one-sided and can produce side-effects almost as unpleasant as the original complaint. Of course, in an emergency, when there is urgent need to reverse a sudden decline in the patient's health, even the most dedicated advocate of herbalism may prefer orthodox treatment. Herbal remedies work slowly and gently and if correctly administered rarely produce side-effects. Though they may be taken for a specific ailment, they service the whole organism and restore harmony where there was imbalance.

While herbalism fell out of favour in Great Britain, it flourished in America. The early settlers there had taken with them the seeds of various herbs, and were taught how to use indigenous species by the Indians. They also made some new discoveries. In a winter harsher than they had anticipated, the food supplies of one group ran out and they had to forage. They found the bark of the Canadian elm to be nutritious and remarkably fortifying — it is still consumed today in the form of 'slippery elm', a drink given to convalescents.

In Great Britain herbalism continued to be thought of as cranky and outmoded until the 1960s. But the tragedy of thalidomide and the many other cases of disastrous side-effects of drugs that have come to the public attention over the last couple of decades have contributed to a renewal of public interest in natural medicine. Today people are once more beginning to feel that 'natural is best'.

Herbs smell good. Crush the leaf of a herb between finger and thumb to get a stronger aroma. What you can smell is the essential, volatile oil of the plant, and it has already done you good with its refreshing aroma. The delicious smell of herbs commonly used in cooking stimulates the salivary glands and the digestive juices — one reason why herbs aid digestion. Besides their essential oils herbs contain mineral salts, such as potassium and calcium, and bitters, which stimulate the digestive juices and the circulation. In addition herbs have other ingredients — glycerols, tannins, saponines and carbohydrates. All interact subtly on the various organs of the body to restore, stimulate and relax, creating a healthy balance.

Culinary herbs and spices will help you cut down on the high levels of salt, sugar and additives like monosodium glutamate which are often added to foods to disguise their bland taste or to stimulate the taste buds. Substitute cumin, basil or nasturtium, which is rich in vitamin C. The flowers, washed, look delightful and taste hot — toss them in salad or put them in sandwiches. The seeds can be ground or pickled — like capers — and the leaves, too, are good to eat, as well as being pretty. Instead of salt, use marjoram or thyme, and in place of sugar try angelica, lemon thyme or sweet cicely.

Animals know instinctively which herbs will be useful to them. Even carnivores like cats and dogs eat grass when they need to be sick. People do not have such powerful instincts and gathering herbs for medicinal and culinary use can be risky unless you are completely sure what you are doing.

Many parts of plants are used in medicine — the roots, stalks, leaves, flowers, bark, berries and seeds — though certain parts of some healing plants can be poisonous and must be avoided. You must also know when in their life cycle to pick them. Some plants are healing when young, but poisonous at seeding time. Some poisonous plants are easily confused with edible plants that look remarkably similar: fool's parsley, one example, has a root like a parsnip.

Do not assume that, because you have seen an animal eating a plant, it is safe for you to eat it too. Sheep eat hemlock — Socrates' suicide draught — and cattle eat henbane, the plant that killed Hamlet's father. (In the hands of a professional herbalist, henbane can be a gentle sedative).

Herbs are at their most potent when the flowers first open. Ideally they should be gathered on a warm morning, after the dew has evaporated and before the sun gets too high. The leaves are at their best before the flowers have started to drop. Hang them in bunches out of the sun in a well ventilated room to dry (unless you are going to eat them fresh); then store the parts of the plant you are planning to use in dark, glass, screw-topped jars in a cool, dim place. Harvest the seeds when ripe and store them similarly. Herbs left hanging in the kitchen may look decorative, but they will collect cobwebs and lose their flavour.

Flowers for herb teas and pot pourris may be dried on a piece of muslin stretched over a child's hoop and suspended from the ceiling.

HERBS

INFUSION

COMPRESS

OINTMENT

POULTICE

To get the best out of herbalism you should, of course, consult a herbalist, who will listen to the various aspects of your case history and prepare an individual remedy. When herbalists 'prescribe' a herbal remedy they prepare it specifically for the needs of the individual patient, the aim being to restore general health and vitality and treat the cause of the symptoms rather than just the symptoms themselves. No two herbalists therefore will quite agree on the precise uses and properties of the same herb plant and many herbals old and new list 20 or 30 possible remedies for just one complaint. For medicinal purposes more than one herb at a time is often used. When herbalists use a single herb (eg garlic, dandelion, rue, camomile, comfrey, parsley or meadowsweet), this is referred to as a 'simple'. Herbalists generally cococt their remedies direct from the plant or from an extract previously extracted as a tincture. This is a concentrated solution of the plant material left to macerate for a period in alcohol and water, then pressed to extract the soluble substance and filtered. Diluted, tinctures form the basis of remedies for internal use or they can be mixed into various creams and ointments for external use. There is no substitute for someone who has studied and understands the properties of herbs but you may also like to visit a health-food shop, where the person behind the counter should be able to help you choose from the range of natural medicines on sale. For the treatment of common ailments you may also want to make a few simple remedies at home from the herbs growing in your garden. Home remedies take various forms.

Infusions and decoctions
Both these are liquids to be drunk. To make an infusion or herbal tea, pour boiling water on to a spoonful of leaves or flowers in a cup and leave to steep for about 10 minutes. Strain and drink while warm. Add a little honey if you like. A more vigorous method is needed to extract the potent agents from roots, twigs, seeds and bark. Put the herbal material into a pan and pour on cold water in the proportion of 1oz (25g) to one cup. Bring to the boil and simmer for 20 to 30 minutes. Cool and strain before using.

Compress
Dip a cloth into a hot or cold infusion or decoction and apply to the affected area.

Ointment
To make an ointment first prepare a small quantity of strong decoction. Strain and add olive or vegetable oil. Return to the heat and simmer to reduce. Add melted beeswax to gain the desired consistency.

Poultice
Crush the plant to a pulp, wrap it in gauze and apply it to the affected area hot or cold. Alternatively, add more herbs to an infusion or decoction and dip a cloth in it. Poultices are an ideal treatment for inflammation, bruises, wounds and abscesses.

HERBS

ABRASIONS ~ Infusion of fresh flowers of St.John's wort in olive oil; lovage.

ASTHMA ~ Fennel; eucalyptus; horehound; elderflower; hyssop; aniseed; liquorice root; pleurisy root; camomile.

ATHLETE'S FOOT ~ Red clover blossoms (boiled); dried comfrey leaves & water; goldenseal root tea; infusion of fresh or dried thyme leaves.

BLEEDING GUMS ~ Sage mouthwash.

BLEEDING NOSE ~ Nettles.

BOILS ~ Teas made from burdock, echinacea, goldenseal, barberry, yellow dock, comfrey, figs.

BRUISES ~ Compress of comfrey; witch hazel.

BURNS ~ Camomile tea (cold); raw onions & potatoes; compress of comfrey.

COLDS ~ Hot elderberry wine (add honey); onions & garlic; camomile; sage; rosemary; peppermint.

CONSTIPATION ~ Dandelion; figs; olive oil; nettles; liquorice; alder; blackthorn; fennel; molasses; prunes; slippery elm; spinach.

COUGHS ~ Elder blossom; sage; calamint; sunflower seed oil.

DANDRUFF ~ Apple cider vinegar; rosemary; sage.

DIARRHOEA ~ Infusion of blackberry root; meadowsweet; cinnamon; comfrey root; elderberry; peppermint; raspberry leaf.

DYSPEPSIA ~ Dandelion; caraway.

EARACHE ~ Mullein oil; plantain.

FATIGUE ~ Peppermint; rosehips; marjoram; agrimony.

FEVER ~ Elder; cayenne; boneset; yarrow; vervain; catnip; tincture of aconite; peppermint tea; yarrow tea.

GUMS (SORE) ~ Sage.

HAY FEVER ~ Wood betony; mullein tea.

HEADACHE ~ Hops; mistletoe; rosemary; wood betony; camomile; mint; poppy; lavender (compress); peppermint tea.

INFLAMMATION ~ Comfrey; plantain; witch hazel (externally); parsley poultice.

INSOMNIA ~ Hops (pillow); lady's slipper root; aniseed; valerian; passionflower; skullcap; camomile; geranium (for sniffing); linden.

MENOPAUSE ~ Lady's slipper; mistletoe.

MENSTRUAL COMPLAINTS ~ Nettle tea; mistletoe; lady's mantle tea; cranberry; parsley; rosehip; mint; tansy (with caution); evening primrose oil; red raspberry leaf tea

MIGRAINE ~ Mistletoe; rosemary; lime flower tea; peppermint tea; feverfew.

NERVOUSNESS ~ Celery; mistletoe; rosemary; damiana; lady's slipper; olive oil; valerian; marjoram.

OEDEMA (FLUID RETENTION) ~ Juniper berries; parsley; celery; cornsilk; fennel.

PILES ~ Lesser celandine; pilewort.

RHEUMATISM ~ Dandelion; celery; rosemary; parsley; cuckoopint (externally); ground elder; hyssop; mugwort; camomile; nettles.

SORE THROAT ~ Red sage tea (gargle); stinging nettle (gargle); garlic; thyme (gargle).

SPRAINS ~ Comfrey oil; arnica.

STINGS & BITES ~ Plantain; oil of eucalyptus; grated onion; horseradish (externally); crushed basil leaves.

TOOTHACHE ~ Oil of capsicum; oil of cloves; elder (held in mouth).

VOMITING ~ Spearmint; camomile; peppermint.

Around the home herbs have always been used to scent the air, their antiseptic properties help guard against infection. Herbs and sweet-smelling grasses were strewn on the floor in Elizabethan times (when the place for a carpet was on the wall). Woodruff was a particularly popular strewing herb and it was also used to rub the furniture, giving it a shine and a fragrance. Many uses of herbs around the home have survived, such as in a pillow for a good night's sleep, in a pot pourri, and in muslin bags to scent the contents of drawers and wardrobes.

At least since Cleopatra's day herbs have been employed for their fragrance and regenerative properties as beauty aids — to improve the skin, give a shine to the hair and a pearly lustre to the teeth and nails. These age-old cosmetics are now coming into fashion again. Here are a few popular recipes.

Cocoa butter
This is a rich cream, especially good for dry skins. Use it as a cleanser or a moisturizer. Take equal quantities of lanolin, cocoa butter and almond oil and melt them together in a saucepan over heat. Transfer to a blender and process, adding just enough camomile infusion (you could use a tea-bag) to make a good, creamy consistency. Allow to cool, then store in a sterilized screw-topped jar in the fridge.

Violet milk
Violets are excellent for the complexion. Fill a cup with violet flowers and pour on warm milk. After several hours, strain and keep in a dark glass jar in a cool place. Soak a pad of cotton wool in the milk night and morning and dab on your face.

Apricot, almond and wheatgerm oil
Blend together equal quantities of apricot, almond and wheatgerm oils and store in a screw-topped jar in the fridge. This is a well-known regenerative treatment. It can be rubbed into the skin to act as a discouragement to wrinkles.

For tired eyes
Apply thin slices of cucumber or potato, or even cold tea bags squeezed of excess tea, to your closed eyelids. Relax.

Rosemary hair rinse To give dark hair depth of colour and shine, simmer rosemary in water for 10 minutes, then mix with cider vinegar. Use when cool as a final rinse after shampooing. Do the same with camomile for fair hair.

Honey-and-glycerine hand lotion
This is a soothing lotion for rough or sore hands. Warm 2 tablespoons of honey in a saucepan and then whisk in 4 tablespoons of glycerine, a few drops of white wine vinegar and $\frac{1}{4}$ to $\frac{1}{2}$ pint of rose water.

Herb waters (for use as skin tonics)
You can choose a variety of herbs or their flowers for these preparations — not just the familiar lavender. Use 2 tablespoons of dried herbs or flowers or approximately 3 handfuls if they are fresh. Pour on 1 pint (50ml) of boiling water, cover and steep for a minimum of 20 minutes or up to one hour. Strain and bottle either by itself or mixed with 2 tablespoons witch-hazel.

Herbs

A herb garden *The time to plant most herbs is spring, either by sowing seeds or taking cuttings. It is said that parsley seeds will never grow unless sown by the woman of the house. Herb gardens of the past were elaborate and extremely decorative, as well as being very restful and fragrantly healthful places to while away the time. They were often laid out in knot gardens, with perennials trimmed into miniature box hedges to divide the beds.*

Garlic *This clears the head and brings relief to anyone suffering from a cold. It expels worms from the intestines, acts on the kidneys, induces perspiration and lowers the blood pressure. It was used to ward off the plague and garlic juice on swabs was applied to soldiers' wounds to reduce risk of infection. Pounded with honey it is good for rheumatism.*

Sage *Much favoured as a strewing herb for its fragrance, sage was also said to retard old age by recharging energy and the memory cells. It is used as a hair rinse to darken greying hair and as a gargle for the throat and mouth. Rub the leaves across your teeth to whiten them and tone the gums.*

Herbs

Rosemary *'Rosemary for remembrance' is something that was repeated long before Ophelia's day. Greek students made garlands of rosemary to wear while taking their exams. It is good for the head in other ways: it is an excellent hair rinse, which tones the scalp, and it relieves nervous headaches.*

Meditation

To aid meditation St. Francis de Salles advised smelling a pink, a rose, rosemary, thyme, jasmine and orange blossoms one after the other.

Crocus

Crocus sativus, *the autumn crocus, is King Solomon's saffron plant. The stigmas only are used, and they are almost worth their weight in gold. The women in Syria and India, where the crocus grows by the acre, collect the stigmas for sale. Some are pounded into cakes. They are used for colouring and flavouring food and for dyeing cloth.*

Frankincense and myrrh

Frankincense is the gum of an Indian tree and is prized as the sweetest of perfumes. Myrrh is a spice valued for its oil, used to anoint the vessels of the Tabernacle.

AROMATHERAPY & PERFUME

79

Aromatherapy

Aromatherapy is the art of using the essential oils of plants as a complete treatment for mental and physical health and beauty. The practice is thousands of years old and was probably first used systematically in China. The ancient Indian medical discipline, the Ayurveda, which is still very much alive today, has always employed plant essences in healing, to combat infection, soothe inflammation and relieve tension and depression. Many Indian women attribute the flawless beauty of their skins to aromatherapy.

The word, aromatherapy, was coined by a French chemist, Gattefosse, in the early years of this century. He was the first European to 'discover' the therapeutic powers of essential oils. Apparently he burned his hand one day in the laboratory, and plunged it instinctively into a bowl of lavender oil to relieve the pain. To his surprise, the wound healed in a very short time and he was left with very little scarring. He set out to investigate the healing properties of other essential oils and his work was continued by the distinguished Austrian biochemist, Marguerite Maury, who explored the effects of aromatherapy on the mental and emotional state of her patients as well as using it in a cosmetic treatment for the skin.

In the course of her research she found that each patient, or client, responded in a slightly different way to a given treatment, so that each 'prescription' had to be tailor-made to suit the woman's chemical make-up, diet and lifestyle. The individual nature of therapy is something that is recognized in all branches of holistic treatment, and it is taken especially seriously in France, where only qualified doctors are allowed to practice aromatherapy.

Even so, it is commonly agreed that certain oils lift the spirits, while others calm them, and that some are particularly good for the skin, while others relieve aches and pains or heal wounds. Ylang-ylang, citrus, basil, patchouli and peppermint are especially recommended to lift depression; geranium, bergamot and lavender relieve anxiety. Rose, neroli (mock orange), fennel and tangerine are good for the skin, peppermint soothes muscular and rheumatic pain, and lavender, as Gattefosse discovered, may help to heal a wound.

How to Use Essential Oils

Oils can be administered in several ways, and the treatment is luxurious. First, the oil should be diluted in a neutral carrier oil. To apply neat essential oil to the skin could cause a burn. You can buy oils ready-diluted, but if you have the concentrated essence, it needs to be mixed in the proportion of 1:50 with a carrier such as almond, apricot, hazelnut, groundnut or safflower oil. Always store essential oils in tightly capped or stoppered dark-glass bottles in a cool place or in the fridge. Essential oils are highly volatile, unlike the fatty culinary oils, and will evaporate quickly if exposed to heat, light or air.

The diluted oils can be applied to the face and body and rubbed

Aromatherapy and Perfume

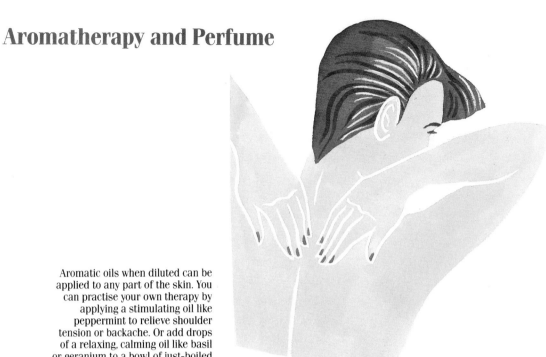

Aromatic oils when diluted can be applied to any part of the skin. You can practise your own therapy by applying a stimulating oil like peppermint to relieve shoulder tension or backache. Or add drops of a relaxing, calming oil like basil or geranium to a bowl of just-boiled water and inhale the fragrant steam.

or massaged into the skin. The base of the spine and the back of the neck are particularly good application points for the relief of nervous tension. You can also inhale directly from the bottle or add one or two drips to a bowl of just-boiled water, bend your head over it and drape a towel over your head and the bowl to keep in the steam. This is particularly effective when using peppermint or eucalyptus oil to relieve breathing problems. Another way to enjoy the oils is to add about 10 drops to a hot bath. Make sure that there are no draughts in the bathroom and have a long relaxing soak, inhaling the perfume at the same time.

You can also make ointments and fragrant waters with essential oils. For an ointment, melt over heat one part of beeswax with five parts of carrier oil. Stir well to combine, then allow to cool. Stir in 10 drops of plant essence and store in a tightly sealed jar in a cool, dark place. Do not add the plant oil while the mixture is hot or it will evaporate. For a room or body spray add about five drops of oil to one pint of water. To scent a room you can also add a few drops of oil to a bowl of water near a radiator.

How Do Oils Work?

There is no doubt that oils are lovely to use and that they have a beneficial effect on the mind and body. It is easy enough to understand why certain smells, such as clean laundry, baking bread or the sweetness of fresh milk, have strong associations of warmth, comfort and nourishment and hence, perhaps, of home and childhood. But it remains a mystery how a particular scent can suddenly revive a memory long since forgotten by the conscious mind and bring with it in a rush the complex of feelings associated with that incident. No one knows, likewise, why oil of camomile should lift melancholy; only that it can. Neither is it possible to manufacture synthetic drugs that reproduce the effects of essential oils. The natural substances have balancing properties that no drugs can match. Oil of garlic, for example, can lower high blood-pressure and raise low blood-pressure. Oil of peppermint calms and stimulates at the same time.

Essential oils are composed of different molecules. Some of these are terpenes, esters, ketones, aldehydes, alcohols and phenols. They are very volatile and some dissolve in both oil and water. In minute water droplets released into the air they can be inhaled. At the top of the nose they are intercepted by the olfactory nerve cells (humans have some 10 million of these, dogs 20 times that many). From there their messages are transmitted to the brain, where they activate responses in ways as yet not understood. When rubbed into the body, the aromatic molecules will be absorbed by the body's natural oil or sebum.

How Essential Oils Are Produced

Manufacturers of essential oils — for aromatherapy and for the perfume trade — have several methods of producing them. The first and most economical is also the most ancient: by distillation. In ancient Egypt cedarwood was put in a clay pot covered with a cloth over a fire. The steam from the wood was absorbed into the cloth, which was repeatedly wrung out, producing essence of cedarwood. Today's methods may be more streamlined, but the principle is still the same.

Expression is the second method, used particularly with citrus rind, which is pressed and squeezed. Extraction is the third method, and this can be divided into two. In enfleurage sheets of glass are coated in odourless fat, into which petals are pressed. The fat gradually absorbs the scent. This is costly and time-consuming and explains why some essential oils, particularly that of the tuberose, are worth more than their weight in gold. It takes 10 tonnes of rose blossom to produce a single kilo of oil. The second method of extraction is solvent extraction using a hydrocarbon solvent such as petroleum spirit which is then boiled off. The method is used to extract the oils of gums and resins and for flowers such as jasmine.

A scene depicted in 1891 showing Queen Victoria visiting the famous perfume factory at Grasse.

Perfume

Wearing perfume gives pleasure, not only because it smells nice, but because it creates an aura around the wearer that expresses something she wishes to convey about her personality. Like make-up, it also acts, of course, as a disguise or mask, as the projection of a desired image which may have little to do with the reality behind it. Perfume is essentially romantic and the use of it is primarily as a sexual signal.

The sexual scent-signals of animals, airborne hormones called pheromones, can be detected over distances of several miles by potential mates, who then home in excitedly on the sender. Pheromones have been isolated by scientists, who can now reproduce them artificially. They are used by breeders to bring animals into heat and by arable farmers to divert harmful insects from their crops. The search for a human aphrodisiac has not been so successful, though efforts have been made to find or manufacture one for thousands of years. Perfume is the most commonly available potion that we are encouraged to believe, at least by the manufacturers, has aphrodisiac qualities.

Aromatherapy and Perfume

How perfume is made

A good-quality perfume may have between 20 and 150 ingredients, mostly of plant or man-made origin, though some are extracted from animals. The vast majority of perfume houses commission their fragrances, which can take about three years to create, from perfume laboratories. The centre of the perfume industry is at Grasse, in the south of France. Here is field upon field of roses, violets, jasmine, lavender and carnations. Cloves, cinnamon, coriander, ginger, patchouli, vetiver and many other plant ingredients are imported from India and the East. The essential oils of these plant materials are extracted and blended by perfumiers (called 'noses' in the business), who may be able to recognize about 800 of the 2000 or so different ingredients in use in the industry at a sniff.

Synthetic ingredients are produced by chemical processes, an increasingly important part in the manufacture of perfume. Not only can they supply entirely new scents unknown in nature, but in some cases they can reproduce a scent, such as that of hyacinth, which does not lend itself to extraction. They are useful, too, because they are often cheaper than natural extracts, especially when there has been a poor harvest, or when climatic and other conditions have not been favourable for the full development of a scent. They are used to supplant the use of animal extracts in many cases.

The chief animal ingredients in perfume are civet, musk and ambergris. The collection of civet, which comes from the sex glands of the civet cat, is an extremely cruel process. The cats are trapped and closely confined in heated cages. Taunting the animals stimulates the secretion of civet, which is scraped from them several times a week over a period of four or five years. To gather musk the musk deer, which lives in India, must be killed. Deer were hunted almost to extinction because of this and are now a protected species. Ambergris is a waxy substance formed in the stomachs of some whales as a result of irritation caused by cuttle fish in their diet. Huge chunks of ambergris, up to 2m (2yd) in length may then be disgorged. They float in the sea around Australia and New Zealand until they are picked up or washed ashore.

As may be imagined, some of these substances do, in fact, smell vile (as do some of the plant extracts), but the end result of a blend of them in perfume is more than a sum of the parts. In this perfume is like music, and they have a vocabulary in common. At the bottom of a perfume are the base notes, heavy and lasting, but slow to develop with the body's warmth. Then there are the middle notes, which describe the character of the fragrance; and thirdly come the top notes, which are light and immediately perceived.

Concentrated perfume (really 20 per cent perfume and 80 per cent alcohol) is very expensive, but probably a better buy than eau de toilette (5-12 per cent perfume mixed with alcohol and water) or eau de cologne (2-6 per cent perfume with water). Once you have bought a perfume use it. It will start to go off about six months after opening, faster if you don't keep it properly. Replace the stopper tightly and put the bottle in a cool, dim place.

Aromatherapy and Perfume

The perfume families

There are four main families of perfume, though any fragrance can borrow notes from one of the others: the florals — cool, elegant and feminine; the chypres (said to have originated in Cyprus) — warm, sensuous and subtle; the greens — clean, uncluttered and fresh; and the orientals — seductive and sultry. The characteristics just noted are the ones advertised by the manufacturer. Think of Opium (Yves Saint Laurent), for example. Then think of Charlie (Revlon). It is possible that you may want to wear Charlie during the daytime and Opium at night, but most women seem to prefer fragrances from one family only.

Choosing perfume can be difficult. When making your selection, try to ignore the advertising if you can. You may fancy yourself in a harem, but you might find the scent associated with that image oppressive. It is best to try only

about four perfumes in one session, say two on each arm, then leave the perfume counter with its confusion of fragrances and make your decision as the perfumes develop on your skin. Don't think what you like on a friend will necessarily suit you. Perfume responds differently to different types of skin.

Perfume can be worn all over, but too much of it can be overpowering to the point of giving you and anyone you may be with a headache. The pulse points — the temples, the nape of the neck, the inside of the wrists, knees and elbows are good places to dab perfume.

Cosmetics have been used in the art of being beautiful by both women and men for thousands of years. The Gauls dyed their hair red with goat's grease and beech ashes; the Anglo-Saxons went punk with green, orange and blue locks; while the Greeks opted for a more sophisticated look, streaking their hair with gold and silver powders. It was the Greeks who were also responsible for popularizing the use of white lead. Powdered on the face, it made a person pale and interesting and covered the ravages of disease, but it eventually ruined the complexion completely — and it continued to wreak havoc with women's faces well into the 19th century.

It was the Egyptians who first manufactured cosmetics on a large scale and the preparations they used are surprisingly similar to today's. The Egyptian lady's eyes were ringed with dusky kohl and her lids shaded turquoise with a powder made from green copper and lead ore. Lips and cheeks were rouged with powdered clay and the palms of the hands, the soles of the feet and fingernails and toenails were given a rosy glow with an application of henna. Hygiene was a priority. Cleopatra bathed in asses' milk, which softened and conditioned her skin, and high-born men and women anointed their bodies with spiced and scented oils. Both sexes shaved their heads and wore intricately styled and elaborately ornamented wigs.

The excavation of ancient Egyptian tombs has revealed beautifully worked cosmetic pots, some of them still containing traces of ointment. Tiny

The History of Make-up

spoons, palettes, bowls and pestles for measuring, mixing and grinding coloured powders have also been discovered, as well as ornamented containers for kohl sticks, bejewelled perfume jars, metal mirrors and hairdressing tools such as combs and curling tongs.

In ancient Rome powerful bleaches and hair dyes were used so rigorously that baldness often resulted. But before the society lady resorted to a wig, she often tried to remedy her problem with pungent conditioners made from dung. While her hair was falling out, she was busy ruining her skin by caking her face and neck, shoulders and arms with white lead.

The bloodless look was brought into vogue in England by Queen Elizabeth I, who used white lead and masks of egg white, ground alabaster and clay to intensify her natural pallor. A pale skin indicated refinement, and every precaution was taken to avoid exposure to the sun. Clothes and head-dresses were cumbersome and difficult to remove, let alone clean, so personal hygiene reached a low ebb and powerful scents, such as civet and musk, were used to disguise un-

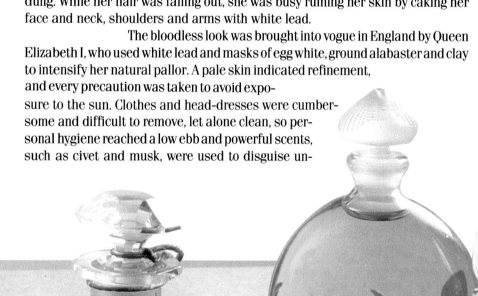

The History of Make-up

pleasant body odours. As Elizabeth aged, she hid her thinning locks under intricately dressed wigs, and painted blue veins on her whitened forehead to create the impression of a youthfully translucent skin.

The 17th and 18th centuries saw even more absurd efforts to counter the effects of ageing. A poor diet, a dissipated lifestyle and the use of white lead meant that the faces of the upper classes were disfigured with pimples and pock marks that no cosmetics could conceal. More serious harm was done to the eyes, which were treated with drops of belladonna — deadly nightshade — to dilate the pupils and simulate sexual arousal. Over-use of belladonna irrevocably impaired the eyesight.

The beaux and belles of the Regency period could not cap these mad excesses. Instead they changed the trend and chose a fresher, more natural look. Make-up became more discreet and less damaging to the skin, and powdered wigs fell out of fashion, making way for softer styles. Cleanliness became easier to achieve, and more desirable. In the Victorian era, personal hygiene became an obsession and home-made herbal preparations enjoyed a tremendous vogue. Make-up was frowned upon as being indicative of an immoral character, and cosmetics had to be applied discreetly and in secret.

Victoria's daughter-in-law, Queen Alexandra, revived the popularity of painted faces, and women were soon copying the exaggerated looks of the stars of music hall and vaudeville. With the advent of the cinema, a chalky complexion, rouged cheeks, dark eyelids, bright, bow-shaped lips and, later, platinum blonde hair became all the rage. World War I liberated women somewhat from the glamour-queen stereotype, as did World War II. Women who worked in factories cropped their hair for safety and convenience and were not embarrassed if they were seen applying their make-up in public.

Lipstick was the most important item in any woman's cosmetic bag. No one felt dressed without bright red lips until the 1960s, when lips paled almost to insignificance beneath hugely emphasized eyes. Black eyeliner, often three layers of it, underlining upper and lower lashes and marking the crease of the eyelid, was supported by hard, brightly coloured eyeshadow and enormously long false lashes. The lower lashes were often painted on to the skin with eyeliner. In the 1970s the hippie movement encouraged a back-to-nature trend and with the advent of the 1980s came a revival of enthusiasm for natural products.

Below: Lana Turner became known as the sweater girl, pin up of World War Two. She was first spotted working at a soda counter in Hollywood and went on to make a number of successful films.

Making Up

Always begin your make-up routine by cleansing, toning and moisturizing the skin. Make-up applied to skin that is not scrupulously clean will clog the pores and will look stale and unattractive. Whether you cleanse with a cream, a milk, or a mild soap and warm water, a toner will put life and freshness into your skin and close the pores. If you have a dry or sensitive skin choose a toner that does not contain alcohol. More astringent preparations can be used on oily skins. If your forehead and nose tend to be greasy and the rest of your face is dry, you would be wise to use two different preparations.

Moisturizers are important for nourishing and protecting the skin. They leave it soft and smooth so that foundation can be applied evenly. To warm up a sallow skin, use a moisturizer that is slightly mauve-tinted. A greenish one will calm down a florid complexion, and a rosy one bring to life a pallid face. Use tinted conditioners sparingly; otherwise you will end up with a green or mauve face.

Foundation

Even the most beautiful skin can misbehave and a foundation will even out skin tones. Foundations are available in liquids or gels, creams, or solid sticks and cakes. Your foundation should be as light as possible — indeed it should not be obvious that you are wearing one. Mask-like faces are very ageing. Your skin looks at its best when it feels alive and glowing with health. The colour of your foundation is important: it should blend as closely as possible with your skin tone to avoid a jarring change at the jaw-line.

Making-Up

Blusher and powder

Once you have experimented with blusher you will realize that it plays an essential part in the art of make-up. It flatters with colour and with shape, too, and careful use of it can make the most of your looks. Blusher in the form of a gel should be applied on top of your moisturizer — don't add powder or you will spoil the gel's translucent shine. Cream blusher is applied over moisturizer or foundation and followed by powder. Powder blusher should be applied over face powder. Gels and creams can be dotted onto the face and blended in with the fingertips, powders dusted on gently with a fat brush. To find out what colour blusher will suit you best, pinch your cheeks and copy the shade of your natural blush. For a highlighter, choose pale peach or ivory for fair skins. If you are dark-skinned or have a tan, gold looks stunning, especially for evening wear.

The positioning of blusher and highlighter is vital. For a heart-shaped face, highlight the cheekbones. The blusher goes on under the cheekbones, sweeping up towards the top of the ear. Broaden a pointed chin with blusher at the tip and highlighter just above it on either side. An oval face needs only gentle shading to emphasize the cheekbones. A round face that tends to plumpness can be made to look thinner by shading the jawline, the cheeks and the area just above the browbone. To reduce the width of the nose, highlight the tip and the sides of it. A square face can be softened by shading from the jawline to the cheeks, and again on the temples.

Below left: use the fingertips to apply liquid foundation evenly over the face, then blend so that there is no visible line between made-up and unmade-up areas. Centre: use a fat brush to dust on powder so that it covers the face then brush in a downwards direction to apply smoothly. Right: apply powder blusher over face powder, sweeping colour lightly under the cheekbones upwards towards the top of the ears.

Top left: a cotton bud or sponge-tipped applicator will help you apply eyeshadow precisely and evenly over the eye lid area. Centre: use a liquid eyeliner or a sharpened eyeliner pencil to define the eyes' outline. Complete the effect by stroking on a thin coat of mascara using a mascara wand (top right).

Eyes

Your eyes are your first and most important contact with another person. They are most expressive of your character and emotions and even if you choose to wear little other make-up, you probably like to emphasize your eyes. You need to exercise care and be delicate in your application of make-up here. Even a dramatic effect is best achieved subtly and with allure. Start with the eyeshadow, remembering to keep all your brushes and applicators clean to avoid irritation or infection.

Both compact and loose eye powders come in vibrant colours and you can moisten the applicator to aid smooth application. Creams and gels are best blended into the shape you want with the tip of the finger. If you are using a pencil colour on the eye, first draw in the shape you want, then blend it with your fingertips. Add highlighter under the eyebrow and on the cheekbones below the outer corner of the eye.

The next step is eyeliner. Carefully paint a fine line close to the lashes, above the upper ones and beneath the lower ones, and colour the rims of the eyes with kohl. Then comes mascara. Whichever type you choose, it always pays to take your time. Several lightly applied coats, with time in between for each to dry, look much more effective than one thick one. Stroke the mascara wand carefully upwards through the upper lashes and downwards through the lower ones. Zigzag the wand gently to avoid clogging. Smudges can be removed with a moist cotton bud; blobs on the lashes with an eyelash brush or comb.

Now brush your eyebrows, first upwards and then into their natural shape. Stray hairs below the brow should be removed when you take your make-up off, but if you spot the odd one, hold the skin taut around around it and tweeze it out smartly, but gently, in the direction of the hair growth. Soft strokes of the eyebrow pencil define the brow. Brush again to disguise the pencil work.

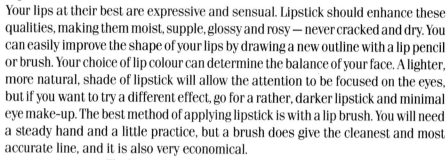

Lips

Your lips at their best are expressive and sensual. Lipstick should enhance these qualities, making them moist, supple, glossy and rosy — never cracked and dry. You can easily improve the shape of your lips by drawing a new outline with a lip pencil or brush. Your choice of lip colour can determine the balance of your face. A lighter, more natural, shade of lipstick will allow the attention to be focused on the eyes, but if you want to try a different effect, go for a rather, darker lipstick and minimal eye make-up. The best method of applying lipstick is with a lip brush. You will need a steady hand and a little practice, but a brush does give the cleanest and most accurate line, and it is also very economical.

The lipstick always goes on after the powder and the fine coat of powder around the mouth with help to keep the lip colour from bleeding upwards in tiny lines. Draw on the outline with a pencil or lip brush, using a slightly darker colour than the one you have chosen to fill in with. If you use a pencil, make sure the point is sharp so that the line you draw is clear and well-defined. Now fill in the lips using a toning colour. Again, a brush is best for this. Blot carefully with a tissue and apply a second coat of lipstick or a generous coat of gloss, being careful not to take it too close to the outline, as it may make the lipstick run. A touch of a lighter shade of the same tone in the centre of the lower lip will make the finished mouth look full and soft.

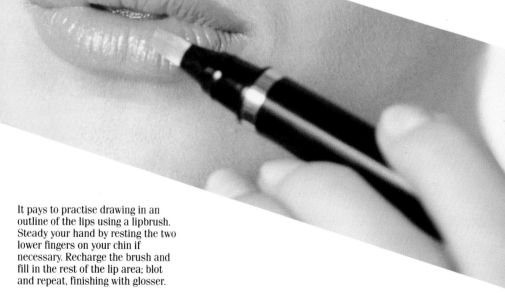

It pays to practise drawing in an outline of the lips using a lipbrush. Steady your hand by resting the two lower fingers on your chin if necessary. Recharge the brush and fill in the rest of the lip area; blot and repeat, finishing with glosser.

Anyone who wants to be proficient in the art of make-up today will find a vast and exciting range of cosmetics to choose from. Be prepared to make a few mistakes before you find out which particular beauty products suit you. Remember that your requirements may change with age, but basically here is what you will need, apart from your skin-care kit of cleansers, toners and moisturizers, to equip yourself.

Blusher Blusher is one of the most important items in your beauty box. Skilfully used, it can transform the shape of your face, minimizing the prominence of features you'd like to disguise and drawing attention to your best points. Choose a cream blusher for use on a cream foundation and powder for a heavier foundation. Two colours, one slightly darker than the other, can be blended into each other on the cheekbones for a more dramatic effect.

Eyeshadow Eyeshadow comes in a huge variety of colours and with a minimum outlay you can equip yourself with everything from subtle shades of grey and fawn, through delicate blues and greens, to stronger harvest colours and striking pinks and purples. Add gold, silver and glitter for extra glamour. Choose your eyeshadow to suit your eye colour, to reflect your mood and to complement your clothes. To 'set' cream eyeshadow, try applying a very fine dusting of translucent powder.

Eyeliner A good kohl stick will produce both a clear line and a more subtle smudged effect. You will need a pencil sharpener, so that you can draw a fine line but always make sure that you round off the end of the kohl to avoid hurting the delicate skin around the eye. A liquid liner will give a more clearly defined effect. You can experiment with various colours, but black is the most useful basic to have and suits most people. Traditional Asian kohl may contain lead and should not be used.

Tweezers For the eyebrows, the most essential thing is a good pair of tweezers to remove stray hairs and give the brows the shape you want. Pluck hairs from beneath the brows and pluck in the direction of the hair growth. A soft brown pencil, used in light, short strokes, will darken the hairs, but be careful not to colour your skin unless you want to create an unnatural effect.

Inside Your Make-up Box

Mascara Most women prefer the liquid mascara that you apply with a wand, as it is less messy than the solid cake variety. If you choose the type with added fibres to thicken lashes, you may need an eyelash comb to remove bits that stick in the wrong places. A mascara without added fibres is normally sufficient, if applied correctly, to make lashes look long and lustrous. Try an eyelash curler used in conjunction with lots of mascara.

Tissues and cotton buds These are necessary for blotting and correcting mistakes. Use dampened cotton wool to remove make-up and if you have forgotten your make-up sponge, use a cotton wool pad wrung out in warm water to apply it. Cotton wool is not as useful near the eyes since fibres can get caught in the lashes. Cotton buds are invaluable for this task: they can be used to smudge eyeliner to make a more natural line and to shade eye shadow so that it blends more softly.

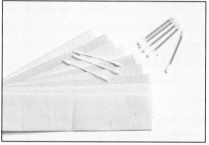

Sponges and brushes Packets of small sea sponges are ideal for spreading foundation. They are long-lasting and do not stain. For powder you can choose a soft, broad brush which will apply the powder finely. For the eyes you will need a shadow brush of medium thickness or a sponge applicator. A short, fat blusher brush or a chisel-shaped lip brush complete this section of your make-up bag. Keep brushes and sponges clean by washing in a mild soap solution, rinsing well and leaving to dry.

Foundation You can choose from liquid, cream or solid foundation, which comes in a stick. Liquid foundations are light, but they tend to streak; creams are generally best for a normal skin. Sticks are useful for covering spots and blemishes. Choose a warm, pink tone for a sallow skin. To tone down a too-pink skin, choose a beige colour. A highly coloured complexion can be toned down with a greenish base, lightly applied, beneath a beige foundation.

Powder Although this is available in many shades and textures, the lightest and most translucent, used over a base that matches your skin tone, is best for a natural look. Powder will keep foundation from streaking and is especially useful, alone or over make-up, if your nose and forehead tend to shine. Avoid a caked look by applying powder very lightly and brushing off the excess with a fine soft brush.

Changing the Shape of Your Face

● **Forehead** A high and broad forehead is best disguised by changing your hair-style, but make-up can also help. Choose a rosy blusher and shade at the temples and down the hairline towards the eyes. Go gently to avoid making a hard line and check your handiwork to make sure that particles of blusher are not clogging the hair. Blend well.

● **Nose** To narrow the bridge of the nose, draw a fine line with shader down the side of your nose from your eyebrow, stopping when you reach the level of the outer corner of the eye. Blend the shadow carefully. To make the nose look more slender, continue the line from the bridge to the bottom of the nose just above the nostril. Blend carefully. If your nose looks too flat, brush a light brown blusher down either side and around the nostrils. Blend a thin line of highlighter down the centre of your nose. To make large nostrils look smaller, apply shader in a thin line with an eye-liner brush in a crescent moon shape around the crease at the side of each nostril. The contour should be widest and darkest at the nostrils. Be sure to blend the line in well so that it is invisible.

● **Chin** To highlight a firm chin or define a receding one, brush cream-toned high-lights on the point of the chin and blend it in. To soften a pointed chin, apply high-lighter under the corners of the mouth in the hollows at each side of your chin. Do not blend yet. Now apply a dot of shader on the point of the chin and blend in all three spots of colour, starting with the shader.

● **Cheeks** To narrow a broad face, apply shader on the fullest part of your cheeks, between the cheek and jawbone. Start the shader just below the centre of the eye and angle it upwards, towards the centre of your ear. Blend well. Now brush on highlighter in a diagonal line above the cheekbones from the outer corner of the eye to the hairline. Widen the diagonal area as you work out towards the hairline and the top of the ear. Blend in well.

Before applying any eye make-up, use a concealing cream, if necessary, around the eyes to hide blemishes that won't be disguised by eyeshadow. Blend this in with the fingertips. Then dust with a thin film of translucent powder, brushing excess away with a small soft brush. Line the lower rims of the eyes with kohl to emphasize the brilliance of the whites. Now you are ready to apply your chosen eyeshadow. Use two shades for well-defined eyes with good shape and depth. The skilful use of eyeshadow can correct the shape of your eyes.

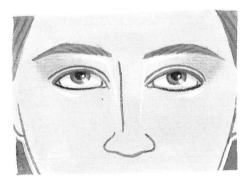

Close-set eyes Brush a pale highlighter on the inside corner of the eye and blend carefully into the side of the nose to make your eyes seem further apart. Next brush a dark-toned shadow onto the outside third of your brow bone, shaping upwards and outwards. If you want maximum definition line the lower rims of the eyes with black kohl pencil.

Small eyes To enlarge small eyes, brush on a light, coloured, powdered shadow with an angle-tipped brush just above your lashes. Apply a darker shadow near the crease. Don't colour near the inner corner of your eye — this will make your eyes look smaller. When applying shadow at the sides, use your brush to blend the powdered shades into one another. Use a light grey pencil under the eye to create a wide-eyed look.

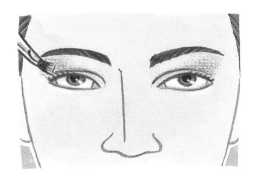

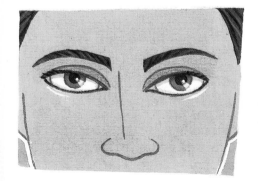

Almond eyes Brush a light-coloured shadow onto your brow bone. Blend in a colour that is a few shades darker on your eyelid. Line the lower inside rim of the eye with black or brown kohl pencil, extending the line out to the corner of your eye. If you have blue eyes, use a blue pencil.

Changing the Shape of Your Eyes

Wide-set eyes With a small blusher brush, apply contour powder that is slightly darker than your skin tone between the eyes and the bridge of your nose. Brush and blend the powder down the sides of your nose. Next brush a neutral-toned highlighter under the outside edge of the brow. Shade the crease line, emphasizing the inner corner of the eye near the nose. Finish by brushing a light matt shadow on the outer corner of the eye.

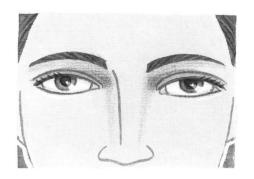

Protruding eyes Shade the entire lid with a medium-coloured to deep-coloured eyeshadow. Never use frosted shades or highlighters: they will emphasize your prominent brow bones and protuding eye sockets. Apply kohl pencil on the lower rims of the eyes. Curl your eyelashes or wear mascara on only the centre lashes.

Deep-set eyes To make deep-set eyes more prominent, brush a pale pink or beige shadow over the eyelid and fade it out above the hollow of the crease. Then apply a medium-toned eyeshadow, starting at the brow bone and blending it up into the brow. Darken the eye area directly over the natural crease with a smoky-coloured shadow that blends well with your other choices. Line the inside lower rims of the eyes with black or brown kohl pencil.

Drooping eyes Starting at the inside corner of the eye, brush a medium-toned shadow upwards and outwards, stopping just short of the brow line. Don't brush any colour on the outer edge of the lid where the eye begins to droop. Instead, create a crease line that is slightly higher than your own by shading it with taupe or medium brown eyeshadow. Curling the lashes will make your eyes look less droopy, as will a few carefully applied coats of mascara.

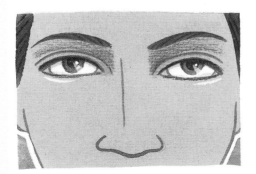

99

Changing the Shape of Your Eyes

Round eyes Choose a deep-coloured shadow and apply it by starting at the inside corner of the eye. Blend the colour in an upward angle towards the outer edge of the brow. Intensify the colour in the corner of the eye and lessen it as you work up towards the brow. Apply a lighter toned shadow or pencil under the lower lid, and extend the colour up and out to blend with the colour below. Dust pale highlighter near the brow line.

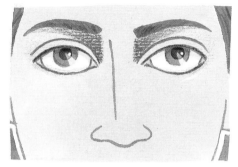

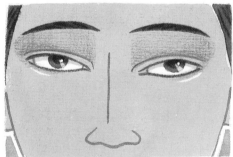

Oriental eyes Brush a pale, matt eyeshadow over the entire lid. Pale pink works well and is a colour traditionally favoured by Oriental women. Now apply a medium-toned eyeshadow on the inner corner of the eye, intensifying the colour closest to the bridge of the nose. Continue blending towards the centre of your eye until the shadow fades out, then brush a darker shade on the outer corner of the eye; blend. Smudge the area below the outside of the lower lashes with kohl in a subtle tone.

- **Full lips** Outline just within the edge of your lips with a lip pencil to minimize full lips. Start at the centre of the upper lip and stroke down towards each corner. Now do the same for the lower lip. Put some colour that is a shade lighter than the pencil onto the lip brush and fill in your lips, starting at the centre and working out towards the corners. The best colours to use to minimize full lips are light rosy shades.

- **Thin upper lips; full lower lip** To give your lips an even fullness, draw an outline beyond the outer edge of your upperlip with the lip pencil, starting at the bow and proceeding with small light strokes to the corners. Follow the natural outline of your lower lip. Fill in the lips with colour on a lip brush.

- **Wide lips** If wide lips bother you, then outline them with a dark-toned lip pencil, fading the line towards the corners of your mouth. Fill in with slightly lighter lip colour. Smudge the outline so that it blends with the lipstick. Avoid shiny or bright lipstick and never wear lip gloss, as these will give the illusion of larger lips.

Enhancing Your Normal Lip Definition

If lipstick is applied alone, without a pencil outline, the resulting splash of colour can make your lips look more imbalanced than they are. Use lip pencils to frame your lips to their best advantage. Remember that your lips should be dry when you apply lipstick.

1 If your lips are dry or cracked, moisturise by brushing on a treatment cream before applying lipstick. The product will also help keep lipstick from running.

2 To define normal lips, use your pencil to draw the outline in small, quick strokes, starting at the brow on the upper lip. This outline also helps to prevent lipstick from smearing.

3 Continue the outline towards each corner of your mouth, keeping it closed and free of tension. Fill in the outline of the bottom lip and prepare the lip brush with colour.

4 Brush the colour, starting at the centre of your upper lip and working outwards; repeat on your lower lip. Depending on the effect you want to achieve, smudge the pencil outline to blend with the lip colour, or leave the outline half visible.

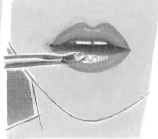

5 For extra shine, dab silver highlighter on the middle of your lower lip. Always blot lips with a tissue.

INDEX